Freedom to learn

An Active Learning
Approach to Mathematics

Freedom to Learn

An Active Learning Approach to Mathematics

Authors
Edith E. Biggs
James R. MacLean

Addison-Wesley (Canada) Ltd.

57 Gervais Drive, Don Mills, Ontario.

Reading, Massachusetts. Menlo Park, California. London

Authors

Edith E. Biggs

James R. MacLean

Foreword

The phrases, active learning, discovery methods, and laboratory approach have become part of our educational jargon during the past few years. What do these phrases mean?

For children, these phrases mean an approach to learning that presents a wide variety of opportunities, an approach that encourages them to ask questions and to find the answers, an approach that fosters the use of physical materials, an approach that gives experience designed to help them analyze and abstract, and an approach that provides a chance to develop their individual potential.

For teachers, these phrases mean an opportunity to explore and discover new and better ways of teaching mathematics, an opportunity to develop an awareness of mathematical possibilities in the environment, and an opportunity to use a highly motivated approach for more efficient education.

This book has been written to assist students preparing for a teaching career, experienced teachers, administrators, and all others interested in children and education to become more familiar with an active learning approach. In particular, we have tried to use mathematics to describe what distinguishes an active learning approach and how it might be implemented.

It is dedicated to all those teachers and their tutors who have helped to make our workshops in many parts of the world lively and entertaining—and hard work for us all! We hope this book will help you to extend and enrich your classroom programs.

Edith Biggs   James MacLean

About the Authors

Addison-Wesley is extremely privileged to publish *Freedom to Learn* by Edith Biggs and James MacLean. Some of the many accomplishments of these two international authors are listed here.

After receiving her degrees from London University, Edith Biggs taught for 16 years in the secondary grammar schools in the United Kingdom. During this time she and a colleague developed and published a series of experimental textbooks. In 1950 she was appointed Her Majesty's Inspector of Schools. In 1964 Miss Biggs was appointed Staff Inspector for Mathematics. She was the author of *Mathematics in Primary Schools,* Curriculum Bulletin number 1 of the Schools' Council, published by Her Majesty's Stationery Office in 1965. In her positions, she has had the responsibility of assisting primary and secondary school teachers in the teaching of mathematics. She also has had the opportunity of working with pupils of all ages from infants through secondary schools. She has directed and participated in workshops for teachers and educators in Rhodesia, Germany, the Far East, Canada and the United States, as well as in the United Kingdom.

James MacLean graduated from the University of Toronto and London Teachers' College of London, Ontario. He taught at various grade levels in both rural and urban schools for 20 years as a teaching vice-principal and principal. In 1960 Mr. MacLean was selected to direct an experimental program in elementary school mathematics. The object of this program was to develop and implement "activity-centered" classrooms. Mr. MacLean's activities and accomplishments include the following: He is a member of the Ontario Mathematics Commission where he has served as Chairman of the Elementary Advisory Committee; he is currently President of the Ontario Association of Teachers of Mathematics; he has published several professional books for teachers; and is currently one of the authors of a new series of elementary mathematics textbooks. In 1966 Mr. MacLean was appointed Assistant Superintendent of Curriculum for the Ontario Department of Education with special responsibility for mathematics. He is presently acting as Program Co-ordinator for the Junior Division. In this capacity he has responsibility of vertical articulation and horizontal integration of all disciplines.

Both authors have written many articles for professional journals and have lectured at professional meetings.

In behalf of Addison-Wesley, I would like to express sincere appreciation for the unlimited co-operation of the authors and also my appreciation to the participants in various workshops and classes whose stories and pictures are recorded in the book by the authors. I feel that this text is a giant step toward establishing a direction for *Freedom to Learn.*

Editor

Contents

Chapter 1   Learning by Doing   1

Chapter 2   How to Make a Start   17

Chapter 3   Classroom Needs   27

Chapter 4   The Role of the Teacher   53

Chapter 5   The Role of the Principal   63

Chapter 6   A Typical Workshop Program   75

Chapter 7   Mathematics and Related Activities for Primary Grades   109

Chapter 8   Mathematics and Related Activities for Upper Grades   141

Chapter 9   Mathematics for the Teacher   163

Chapter 10   Keeping Track: Planning, Assessing, Reporting   185

Chapter 11   A Look at the Future   195

Acknowledgments

Miller Services Ltd., Toronto: photo p. 154.

National Film Board, Ottawa: photos pp. 16, 97, 130, 147.

North York Board of Education: Pineway Boulevard Public School, principal and staff, for allowing us to photograph pictures for this text; Zion Heights Junior High School, for report form, p. 193.

Paul Park, Professor of Science, Althouse College of Education, University of Western Ontario, London: photos pp. 59, 79, 199.

Robert C. Ragsdale, a.r.p.s., Toronto: frontis-piece and chapter opening photographs, photos pp. 38, 45, 48, 162, 190, 199, 200, 201, 202.

Toronto Board of Education: the poem "Justice" by John W. Sullivan. Reprinted with permission from *The Toronto Education Quarterly,* Autumn, 1967; published by the Toronto Board of Education.

Design by Dennis Mason

Illustrations by Brian Moore

Chapter 1

Learning by Doing

Introduction

1-1   Child—Centered Program

1-2   Individual Differences

1-3   Stages of Development

1-4   Children's Strategies

1-5   Meaningful Practice

1-6   Assignment or Task Cards

1-7   Active Learning

Chapter 1

Learning by Doing

This book has been written for teachers and for those who aspire to become teachers. We think it will help those individuals whose devotion to children has made them aware of the shortcomings of the present organization and those who are seeking more effective ways of meeting the needs of the children they teach. We have drawn heavily on our own experience as well as that of the many hundreds of teachers with whom we have worked.

We think it will help teachers who have participated in in-service sessions and have made a start in their classrooms but who need encouragement, more ideas and further mathematical background.

We also think it will help principals and teachers to organize in-service training courses for their colleagues in their own schools or in their own school systems.

Ultimately, we hope it will help children. In the classroom, students will catch the teacher's enthusiasm once opportunities are provided for them to become involved in the learning process. Dr. Z. P. Dienes described the classroom situation we want to create when he said: "It is suggested that we shift the emphasis from teaching to learning, from our experience to the children's, in fact, from our world to their world." The aims of learning mathematics in this active, creative way are:

1/ *to free students, however young or old, to think for themselves.*

2/ *to provide opportunities for them to discover the order, pattern and relations which are the very essence of mathematics, not only in the man-made world, but in the natural world as well.*

3/ *to train students in the necessary skills.*

These aims have inescapable implications for us as teachers. We need to be challenged to think for ourselves and to become aware of the mathematical possibilities of the environment. If we are to spark children's mathematical imaginations, we must first rekindle our own.

School systems of today function much like dinosaurs of the past – it takes a long time for a message from the brain to get the whole organism moving. A few schools, scattered throughout the world, are responding with some speed to a message which has been repeated with increasing urgency for more than 300 years. It is a simple message – schools should be organized, not for teachers to teach but for children to learn. The belief that learning and teaching are concomitant has prevented for many generations the development of truly functional buildings and programs. It has taken us a long time to accept the advice of the few great educational leaders in western life.

Froebel demanded that children should be treated as children and that childlike characteristics such as curiosity should be utilized in education. Pestalozzi tried to get away from a method of teaching that was all words, insisting that wherever possible, children should also learn by touch and sensation. The report of a recent Unesco conference suggests that the more the senses can be involved, the more efficient learning will become.[†] If a child only hears, but does not see, he does not learn as well as if he hears and sees at the same time. If he can touch as well as hear and see, he will learn far more soundly.

This approach through the senses is well illustrated in some recent British films, such as *Maths Alive, Maths is a Monster* and *I Do and I Understand*. (See section 3-5.) Psychologists have learned that the greater the variety of situations to which a child must accommodate his behaviour, the more flexible his attitude becomes. Lack of variety and poor quality of stimulation, can spell deprivation for any child. The pupil of the electronic age requires an educational environment that allows him maximum participation in discovery; schools must relate and synthesize rather than linearly fragment knowledge; they must provide a multiplicity of stimuli that will spark the child's curiosity and engender a continuing desire to learn. The report, *Living and Learning,* suggests that "A school should serve all its children comfortably and humanely in its on-going *child-centered* programs and a learning experience should be found to meet the needs of each . . . ."[‡]

School is almost synonymous with *teacher.* It is the teacher who will determine the direction and extent of any educational reform. "In any field of human endeavour, programs of improvement are successful to the degree that they are understood, accepted and applied by those who have the ultimate responsibility for implementing them. Changes in education, no matter how sweeping, profound or ideal, are barren unless they bring about changes in the classroom; their effectiveness is determined almost entirely by the teacher."[‡] Scientists and researchers in education have not always related their conclusions to the classroom and have frequently failed to convince teachers of the need for change. This may be one of the reasons for the wide gap between learning theories and classroom practice.

The purpose of this book is to translate a generally accepted theory of the learning process into practical suggestions that may be adopted or adapted by the teacher to suit a wide variety of classroom situations. While we are using a particular discipline, in this case, mathematics, as the vehicle to develop an attitude toward learning, we firmly believe that the same approach can be applied to other subjects.

Mathematics has long been considered the most rigidly sequential subject in the curriculum and the first aspect taught was invariably arithmetic. If we can use the natural experiences of children to develop the basic ideas of mathematics in the fields of number, measurement and shape, while maintaining reasonable computational skill, we will avoid much of the criticism being directed at many of the "modern" mathematics programs. Children will enjoy mathematics because it will have relevance to them in the lives they are living; they will appreciate the power and beauty of mathematics because they can use it to communicate their ideas. Moreover, they will recognize the need for a socially acceptable vocabulary of mathematical terms if their discoveries are to be communicated, and they will learn that mathematical activity can be fired by almost any experience, whether it be in science, social studies, music, or any other discipline.

Our experience with young children has shown us that we do not yet know how much mathematics children can learn. The assignment of certain topics or skills to particular grade levels has been a straitjacket which has stifled thought and destroyed enthusiasm. We have grossly underestimated the power and extent of children's thinking. Obviously, there is no one tool or technique that will cut through the bonds imposed by inadequate knowledge and cemented by tradition. We need to apply all our new knowledge of biology, psychology and education to changing the conditions which affect learning. The most significant of these, at the moment, is the shift from emphasis on content to emphasis on experience. In *Living and Learning* we read, "It is wise to let the child be one's guide in opening the doors to learning."[†]

[†]*Mathematics in Primary Education: Learning of Mathematics by Young Children,* International Studies in Education (Hamburg, Unesco Institute of Education, 1966).

[‡]The Provincial Committee on Aims and Objectives of Education in the Schools of Ontario, *Living and Learning* (Toronto, The Publications Office, Ontario Department of Education, 1968) p. 55.

[‡]Ibid., p. 121.

[†]Ibid., p. 55.

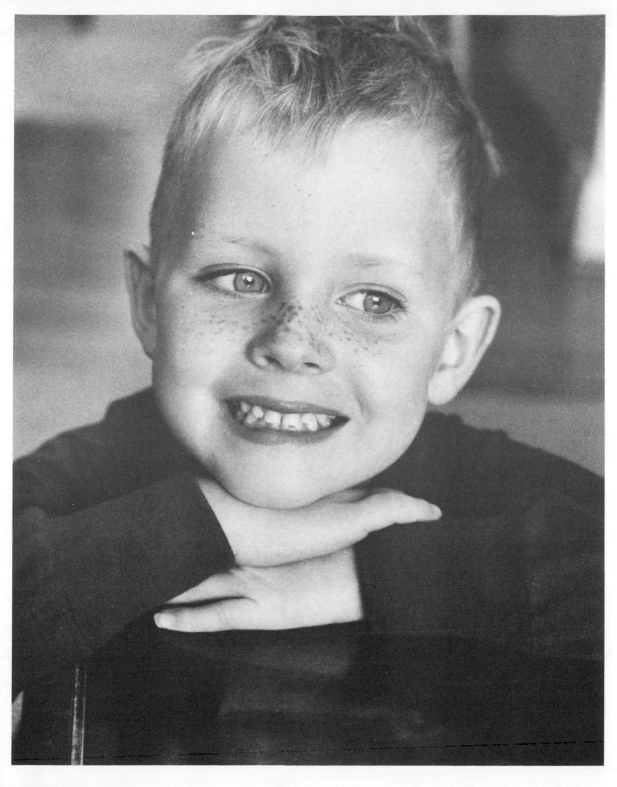

*Children enjoy learning when it is
related to their interests*

Aims like these are inspirational — but to teachers looking for ways of attaining them in practice, they are quite inadequate. If learning is experiencing, which is merely a restatement of the old adage, "we learn by doing," then some provision must be made for the wide range of abilities and interests that exist in every classroom. Providing for individual differences and ensuring continuous progress has been the objective of many organizational schemes in Canada and in the United States. These have improved the classroom climate to some extent for some students, but they have not yet gone very much beyond the one-text-per-pupil-per-grade concept that has shackled our curriculum planners for years. In fact, the idea of a program, whether it be a textbook or a detailed prescriptive syllabus or a course of study, runs counter to current educational thought. What is needed is a broad framework or general guide within which teachers working alone or in groups may develop programs suitable for the children they teach. Only in this way can we acknowledge the unique responsibility of the individual teacher in identifying and meeting the needs of each of his pupils.

Many teachers find that courses of study, timetables, specific textbooks, standard report cards, external examinations and the oft-times iron curtain of subject specialization are almost insurmountable barriers to the kind of classroom they want to create. Usually these difficulties are imposed by some higher authorities whose contact with children is so remote that "they" do not understand or appreciate the problems of students or teachers. The question is not *Can these difficulties be overcome?* but *How shall we overcome them?*

Let us consider how the present traditional classroom can be organized to create an atmosphere for learning that is truly child-centered. How can we respect the child's interests, his dignity, and his individuality while granting him freedom and responsibility?

The first step is to assure teachers that such a climate is attainable and is right for the children they teach. This is particularly difficult because many teachers have never experienced it either as students or as adults. However, conviction does come with successful experience and it is through pre-service and in-service activities that a start can be made.

It should be emphasized that it is an *attitude toward learning* that we are attempting to develop, rather than specific techniques such as workshop or laboratory methods. It is a mistake to apply a label to the innumerable activities and ideas that teachers will use to meet the needs of individual students. Furthermore, such a label implies that there is only one way to implement such a program when, in reality, there are as many ways as there are teachers. Identical patterns of classroom organization for all teachers are just as absurd as uniform standards of achievement for all children. Each teacher must be free to adapt the basic principles to suit his own personality and capabilities, as well as those of his students. "The modern professional teacher is a person who *guides* the learning process. He places the pupil in the centre of the learning activity and encourages and assists him in learning how to inquire, organize, and discuss, and to discover answers to problems of interest to him."[†]

Teachers must have the opportunity to explore and to discover in the same way as the children. This experience has the following advantages: it gives teachers insight into the learning process and helps them to appreciate the excitement and benefits of learning by discovery; it gives them ideas to try out in their own classrooms and opportunities to discuss problems with other teachers; it helps to increase and extend their own mathematical background.

1-1. Child-Centered Program

The major difference between a traditional program and a program which includes some active learning situations is the shift from mainly an authoritarian, teacher-dominated classroom, to a child-centered one; from a program emphasizing content to one using the experiences of children to build concepts and strategies. It must be stressed that there is no magic wand that will transform any classroom overnight. It takes time. The only magic that will affect the program is the conviction and enthusiasm of the teacher, tempered with wisdom. Some overly hasty

[†]Ontario Report, *Living and Learning*, p. 122.

teachers think that everything labelled "traditional" is bad and must disappear, while all that is "modern" is good and should be implemented as swiftly as possible. But no method is a panacea. Just as traditional teaching sometimes produced boredom and poor learning habits, so can the new. No method is better than the teacher who is using it. However, an approach which takes into account both the nature of children and the reasons for education is more likely to be successful.

The image of the teacher as the fountain of all knowledge occupying the front-and-centre of the classroom, dominating and directing all activity, must disappear. There will always be a place for exposition by the teacher, for an account of something interesting and important, whether it be to an individual, a small group, or the whole class. The only difference is that more teachers will be doing what the best teachers have always done. They do not *give* or *teach* a lesson but provide a focus for discussion. The children are encouraged to comment and to ask questions as the lesson proceeds. It is at this stage that the teacher's skill and his recognition of individual needs is so important. He must not be too quick to cut off seeming irrelevancies or to label responses as incorrect or silly. Dr. Albert Schweitzer suggested that "Only those who have respect for the opinions of others can be of real use to them." Do we as teachers show respect for children by our reactions to answers that do not fit our preconceived adult expectations? A child never gives a *wrong* answer! Every problem response that he makes is right for him on the basis of his present knowledge and background of experience. A relationship of mutual trust and respect, in which coercion and punishment have no place and where marks and rewards are unnecessary, is the kind of relationship which distinguishes a "modern" classroom from the "traditional" one.

The reward is great. Where this relationship of trust and respect has been established a good atmosphere for learning exists. John Blackie in *Inside the Primary School* describes it best:

"The children feel free and relaxed and at the same time, in the care of someone whom they respect and to whose authority they can trust themselves."[†] It is not possible to provide a formula or recipe that will guarantee this outcome. Different teachers manage it in different ways, but the relationship is always unmistakable.

The practice of giving the children something to do or learn and then correcting it has a place in the modern classroom as well as in the traditional one. There will always be facts that must be memorized and skills which must be practised. The difference between the traditional and modern approaches to memorization may be illustrated by the student's reaction in the following instance.

The regular teacher had been working hard for several months to achieve the relationship with her pupils that characterizes a child-centered classroom. While she was away for three weeks, the local authority assigned a temporary teacher to the class. After two days the new teacher reported to the principal that the children, ranging in age from 8 to 10, could not add or subtract. The principal, anxious that an unfavourable and unfounded opinion should not circulate throughout the city about this experimental class, investigated immediately.

"How do you know they can't add or subtract?" he asked.

"I gave them a test," she replied.

"What test?" was the further query. The substitute teacher opened a textbook and pointed to two tests on facing pages. The first one had 27 questions on column addition and the second had the same number of subtraction exercises.

"I gave them plenty of time to do them all but their scores were terrible," complained the teacher. With the text in his hand, the principal walked into the classroom and questioned one of the more capable boys about his poor results.

"Billy," he said, "why did you only get seven of these addition questions done?" Billy looked up at the principal with some bewilderment, evoked perhaps by the accusing tone in his principal's voice.

"Sir," he replied, quietly and honestly, "I did the first seven correctly; how many do I have to do to show her that I can add?"

†John Blackie, *Inside the Primary School* (London, Her Majesty's Stationery Office, 1967), p. 37.

The time-honoured motivation, *do this to please the teacher,* was missing in this classroom. The students were fully prepared, even anxious, to acquire the skills they needed to solve the problems that had meaning for them. They were not inclined to waste their time doing boring and repetitious exercises involving skills they had already acquired or for which there was no apparent need. The regular teacher had taken a long first step toward the establishment of an atmosphere of mutual trust and respect. The students were responding with enthusiasm, enjoyment, and sustained hard work to the challenge of increased responsibility for their individual programs.

1-2. Individual Differences

Another significant difference between traditional teaching techniques and what may be called modern strategies for learning is the provision of opportunities for the continuous progress of individuals. It is necessary to decide whether teachers and principals should spend their time dropping children into neat little slots in a graded program or whether their energies would be better spent in devising individual programs for children. The more the actual experiences of children are used as the source of classroom activities, the less difficulty teachers have in making the work interesting and closely related to the needs of individuals. To decide just when a child is ready to learn something new requires a great deal of skill and experience. It is this kind of skill combined with the art of devising or contriving situations where every child experiences some success each day that distinguishes the truly professional teacher from the technician. When children work in an atmosphere that is positive and encouraging, when the problems they face are real to them and their honest effort is rewarded with success, when they are set free to think for themselves, the results will astonish even those who know them best — their parents.

Sir Alec Clegg, a prominent educationalist in England, in a recent speech, gave courage to all teachers who attempt to create an individualized program that provides for continuous progress: "It is a source of great inspiration to me that these fire-kindling ways of using knowledge have made it possible for teachers working in primary schools set in the worst social conditions of the heavy industrial area of the south Yorkshire coalfields to achieve the highest standards I know, and not in one school, but many. And by highest standards I mean the highest standards in behaviour, in reading, in mathematics, in written English, in art, in physical education, in the whole gamut of primary education . . . . They choose the medium in which they work and the topic on which they work. Because a child has chosen his way of working, his medium of expression, his sources of information and his rate of progress, he is not thrown into disheartening comparisons with his better endowed fellows. His relationship with the teacher is more normal — it is now the teacher, not the child, who speaks when he is spoken to."

1-3. Stages of Development

It is not the purpose of this book to describe the many different views on the theory of learning, yet the work of Jean Piaget of Geneva deserves consideration because his theories support the practical classroom techniques which we have found to be most successful. There are many books which attempt to summarize Piaget's views[†] (as well as translations of his own works) that will provide details of the numerous experiments on which he based and refined his theories. The brief description presented here is intended to show the relation between theory and practice and to offer some evidence to support the intuitive judgments of experienced teachers.

Children, says Piaget, begin to develop patterns for learning as soon as they are born. In their early years, the natural curiosity children have about themselves and their environment leads them to the most intense learning of their entire lives. They cannot learn by being told. They must see, hear, feel, smell and taste for themselves.

[†]The following two texts are suggested:

N. Isaacs, *New Light on Children's Ideas of Number* (London, Ward Lock Educational Company, 1964).

K. Lovell, *The Growth of Basic Mathematical and Scientific Concepts in Children* (London, University of London Press, 1961).

Hot, sharp, wet have no meaning for children until they actually experience the physical sensation associated with each word. Piaget suggests that they learn from their own movements too. Learning at this stage is in the sensory-motor field. Children soon find out that they cannot touch everything they see. They must crawl or roll over to reach a desired object. Later they can judge a distance and much later still they can understand what is meant when they are told a distance — the river is two miles wide. As they grow older their patterns of behaviour begin to include patterns of thought. They can assimilate abstractions and accommodate themselves to them.

Piaget emphasizes two things about active learning. First, a child must be allowed to do things over and over again and thus reassure himself that what he has learned is true. Secondly, this practice should be enjoyable. Anyone who has observed the look of sheer joy that enlivens the face of a young child when he succeeds in opening a door, standing up on skates, or solving a puzzle will support Piaget on this point. Unfortunately, not many adults regard this as learning. Many still equate learning with work, and work with discomfort or unpleasantness. In fact, one of the most difficult problems for progressive teachers to overcome is the suspicion that many parents have for programs which their children obviously enjoy. "If they like school that much they can't be working hard enough to learn anything." More will be said later about the play aspect of learning.

In addition to his theory about the learning process, Piaget spent much time investigating how children learn mathematics. He was particularly interested in the concepts known as "conservation" and "reversal." Conservation of number, for example, means the recognition that the number of objects in a set remains the same, regardless of how the objects are arranged or combined. Piaget investigated the various stages that children go through in acquiring this concept as it applies not only to number, but also to substance, weight, length, area, volume and time. Reversal means recognition that if a physical process is reversed a return to the original starting point is made. If a child has twelve chocolates and takes away seven he has five left. When he adds seven back to five he has twelve once more. Piaget assigned the various stages in acquiring these concepts to approximate ages. In general, his findings have been confirmed by other researchers in Britain, Canada and the United States, although there was some inconsistency as to type of response and variability from child to child of the same age.

1-4. Children's Strategies

The significance of Piaget's research for teachers is that we cannot teach children number, length, time, etc. in isolation from natural experience of the environment. It is only through action that the mental operations are developed and co-ordinated. If children must go through the stages that Piaget describes, it is no use trying to teach them something for which they are not ready, though teachers can do much to help them to become ready. The problem is to know what mathematical concepts, processes and facts individual children are ready to learn. The solution is to provide relevant materials in sufficient quantity and variety. Then we must be prepared to encourage understanding, to assist the growth from one stage to the next, to detect this growth when it happens, and open the way ahead. This will involve constant participation by the teacher and much discussion between teacher and children and among the children themselves. Teachers must abandon their adult preconceived expectations of how children will respond to a specific problem or challenge. Examples of the great variety of strategies that children use when they are given the opportunity to think for themselves are revealed in the following accounts of actual classroom situations:

Each one of a class of ten-year-olds had been finding the area of his foot by counting squares (if he had traced his footprint on 1" squared paper) or by covering his footprint with 1" squares (if he had traced it on plain paper). Randy insisted that it was not necessary to count squares. Instead he found the perimeter of his foot using a

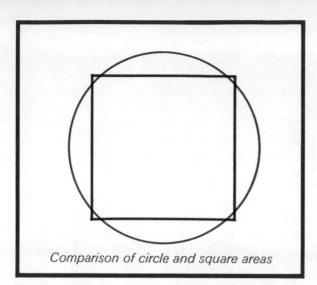

Comparison of circle and square areas

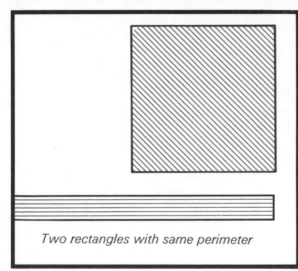

Two rectangles with same perimeter

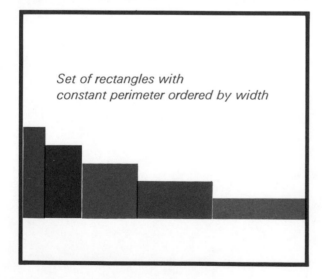

*Set of rectangles with
constant perimeter ordered by width*

piece of string and then arranged the string to form the boundary of a square. From this he found the area of the surface his string now enclosed. He was asked to find the area of his foot by the other method as well. Somewhat reluctantly he did so. The rest of the class, after hearing Randy describe his method, decided to test it. Before anyone began, Margaret quietly stated: "It will give a larger area because the square has the largest surface." The other students found, one by one, that Randy's method was inaccurate because it gave too large an answer each time.

When a group of nine- and ten-year-olds were told this story they were determined to find the largest possible shape they could make, using a fixed perimeter. They experimented with equal loops of string of different colours. To find the smallest area they could enclose, some rolled the string into a spiral while others pulled it taut. A boy with a loop of ribbon announced that he could squash out all the area! A square, a circle and a triangle were superimposed to compare the areas. To make circles the children used ½" strips of construction paper, as string proved difficult to handle. Maurice was so surprised that these areas were different that he checked to see if the lengths of his loops were the same. John and Margaret used a geo-board to help them make a nearly circular shape and to place the square symmetrically within it (fig. 1). They showed the group that the "pieces" outside the square were much larger than the "pieces" outside the circle.

The group next decided to find the largest rectangle they could enclose with their loops. They knew intuitively that this was a square. They set out to explain why. It was Maurice who first thought of arranging a square and rectangle as in figure 2. He explained carefully, in his own words, why the area of rectangle A would always be larger than the area of rectangle B.

Other members of the group then made a table showing:

How the length changed with the width.
How the area changed with the width.

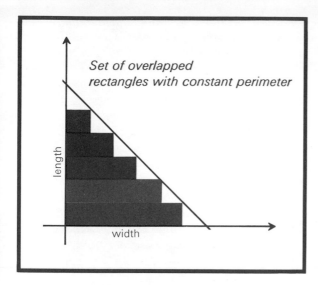

Set of overlapped rectangles with constant perimeter

length

width

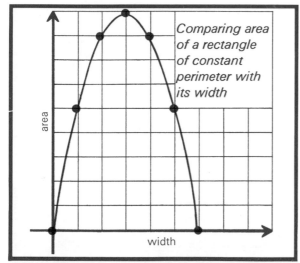

Comparing area of a rectangle of constant perimeter with its width

area

width

Making sets of rectangles with constant area

In the first table the children made, they did not put the widths in order and they did not start with zero. Later Maurice suggested that they should do this so that no possible rectangles would be forgotten. The teacher then suggested to the children that they should cut out each rectangle in their table. The children soon verified that the square had the largest area.

The rectangles were arranged in order of width on the desk. The teacher asked, "What would happen if you moved the rectangles to one corner of the desk so that they overlap?" Maurice had already decided that the top right-hand corners would be in a straight line and was delighted to find that they were. The children noticed that this rearrangement had created a width axis, w, and a length axis, l.

Another group of children drew a graph showing the relationship between the area and the width when the rectangles had a constant perimeter of twelve inches. This showed clearly that a square of 3-inch sides has the largest area of all the rectangles. When their teacher turned on the drinking fountain in the corridor the children were delighted to find the resemblance between the smooth curve of their graph and the jet of water.

On the next day the teacher asked the same group of children if they could reverse the problem they had been considering. "Fix the area instead of the perimeter," said John. After some discussion the teacher asked each child to choose a number less than 20. She then asked the children to draw as many rectangles as they could on the floor; each rectangle was to have an area in squares (tiles) equal to the number chosen and the perimeter had to be determined. The children who had chosen areas of 5 and 7 squares found this very dull and decided to investigate the perimeters of various shapes made with the set of squares they had chosen. The teacher was interested to notice that no matter what shape the children made they usually counted the edges one at a time to obtain the perimeter and often did this twice as a check. The floor soon became covered with shapes, so the children decided to use one-inch coloured squares instead and to mount them on construction paper.

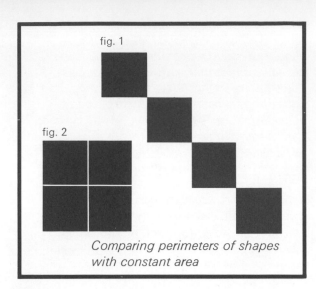

Comparing perimeters of shapes
with constant area

A boy experimenting with 4 squares triumphantly showed the teacher that he had found the largest possible perimeter, 16 units (fig. 1), and also the smallest perimeter, 8 units (fig. 2). "What about trying a number which is not a perfect square?" the teacher asked. He then chose 24. When asked which was the rectangle with the largest perimeter the children answered immediately: "A long thin rectangle." The teacher then asked them to see if they could discover anything special about rectangles with the same area. Most of them chose as the constant area a number with several pairs of factors: 12, 16, 24, 36. This time some of the children decided for themselves to cut out those rectangles with whole numbers of inches as measures of the

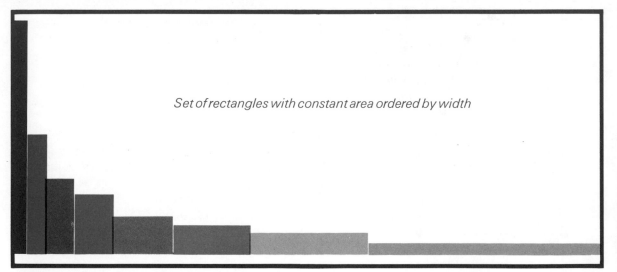

Set of rectangles with constant area ordered by width

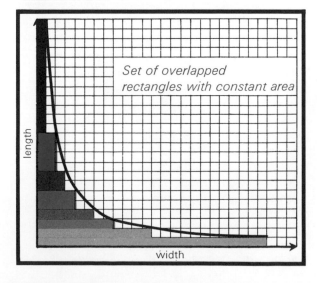

Set of overlapped
rectangles with constant area

sides and with area 24 square inches. They then arranged them in order beginning with the narrowest. No one thought of overlapping the rectangles on the corner of the desk as before. This is a very interesting display as it shows the relationship which exists between the width and the length. The children made a table showing the corresponding widths, lengths and perimeter. From this they plotted:

The ordered pairs: width and length.
The ordered pairs: width and perimeter.

Most children discovered the relationship between the width and the length; others were able to supply ordered pairs but could not verbalise the relationship. No child in the group was able to state an algebraic relationship between the perimeter and the width. They noticed the symmetry in the table they made. They were so surprised at the outcome that they checked all their results and added some intermediate data before they joined the points they had plotted by a smooth curve.

1-5. Meaningful Practice

It has been said that the only time children have the opportunity to think for themselves is before they get to school and it is in this period that they do their best learning. John Holt in his book *How Children Learn* accuses schools of teaching children to think badly, of forcing them to give up a natural and powerful way of thinking in favour of a single method that does not work well for them. Moreover, it is one which we rarely use ourselves. The purpose of our book is to help teachers make their classrooms into places where children can use and improve the techniques and strategies that have worked so well for them earlier. Whether this type of classroom is described as laboratory, workshop, or activity-approach does not matter. The important thing is an atmosphere which encourages resourcefulness, self-confidence, independence, patience and competence. The children may be working individually or in groups. They will be doing different things — handling materials, measuring, discussing, recording. The practice of computational skills is based upon the practical activities in which the children are engaged. In this way, the pupils understand and appreciate the need for polishing and expanding these skills. Contrast this experience with the traditional technique of teaching the process first and then having the students do several pages of examples.

Some six- and seven-year-olds who had been comparing the capacity of a variety of bottles and containers were surprised to find that three bottles of very different shapes held the same quantity of macaroni. They were then asked to estimate the number of pieces of macaroni in a bag. Their first guesses were quite wild, so their teacher

asked them if they could get a better estimate without counting every piece of macaroni. "Count in twos or tens," was the first answer. One girl suggested finding half, counting the number of pieces in half the bag, and doubling.

When the teacher held up a small container and asked the children if they could use this to solve the problem, two suggestions were made:

"Fill the container and count the pieces; count how many times you can fill the container from the bag of macaroni."

"Empty the container-full into a jar with straight sides. Mark the level. Empty the bag into the jar and see how far up it goes. Mark off the units."

These two suggestions represent two entirely different levels of thinking.

There were 110 pieces in the container and it took 6 1/2 containers to empty the bag. A boy paired the containers-full, counting 220, 440, 660. Another boy volunteered: "I know half of 110, because half of 100 is 50 and half of 10 is 5. That makes 55." To their teacher's surprise, they quickly found the total of 715. These children had not worked with numbers of this magnitude before.

This type of experience can give a natural introduction to subsequent work on multiplication.

Some disadvantaged ten- and eleven-year-olds were working on a similar problem, but the numbers involved were far larger. Once more, the four children concerned suggested different ways of solving the problem:

"Weigh and count the number of pieces in an ounce."

"Weigh the bag and add up the number of pieces in each ounce."

"Count the number of pieces in a container and also the number of containers needed to empty the bag." There were 57 pieces in a container and it took 40 containers-full, to empty the bag. For some minutes, no one could decide how to find the total. Then a girl ran to the chalkboard and began to write 57's, one underneath the other. She had thirteen 57's in the first column and

*twelve in the next, when the bell for recess rang —
so the problem was postponed. The next day,
the teacher, concerned about this difficulty,
began by giving the group multiplication
questions from the text, including 40×57.
Each child obtained the right answer by
multiplication, but was totally unaware that he had
therefore solved the problem of the previous day.*

The two contrasting activities of these groups
suggest very forcibly that children need to meet
situations which give rise to the operations of addition, subtraction, multiplication and division before
they are taught the written processes. They can
be helped to devise and refine their own methods.
The children in the second example could be
given practice in counting collections (for a purpose, if possible!) until they realize for themselves the convenience of counting in tens (organizing the collection in groups of tens so that the
whole can be easily checked).

1-6. Assignment or Task Cards

One of the very real problems that faces teachers
in the transition from a traditional to a child-
centered program is how to provide for the different
interests and abilities that exist in every classroom.
How can a program be flexible enough to provide
for individual differences and allow for continuous
progress without a great amount of planning
and organization by the teacher? One of the most
promising resources is the use of individual or
small group assignment or task cards. These are
cards of various sizes with a problem stated on
each one. They can be purchased from commercial
sources, designed by teachers working alone or in
groups, or created by the children themselves. As
with all other devices, the worth of these cards
depends on their suitability for the children who
use them. Generally, each assignment or task
card should incorporate these two principles:

1/ *The children must do something: go out and
measure, design experiments, organize tables of
facts, improvise techniques for comparing weight,
volume, capacity, etc.*

A clue or hint of direction may be given, but it
should be minimal to encourage discussion
and experiment. (The problem is really one
of avoiding ambiguity while keeping the question
as "open" as possible. This becomes easier to do
when you get to know your class and involve
the pupils more and more in the preparation
of assignments.)

2/ *The children must record their findings in some
way that will communicate their procedures and
conclusions (by speaking, writing, drawing, etc.).*

Some assignments will demand a definite
numerical answer that can be marked right or
wrong. These should be in the minority. Other
cards will lead to the discovery of a relationship;
for example, the length of a side to the area
of a square. Still others will have no specific
purpose other than encouraging interest in a new
field of mathematics. Assignment cards for any
group of children should probably include
questions in all categories.

The great difficulty in preparing assignment
cards is to write open-ended questions which
challenge children to think, yet are unambiguous.
It is always possible to close an open question
if a child shows that the problem is too difficult
for him. But, a closed question in the first instance
may well give the child a clue he does not need,
thus depriving him of the opportunity of thinking
and discovering for himself. It is essential for
teachers to aim at providing open assignments
as soon as children show they are ready for this
challenge. Slower children, however, may require
questions which give them more help. It is most
important that all children be made aware that
they have taken the final step on their own (however small that step may be).

Children can eventually be encouraged to
devise interesting questions for themselves. Sometimes these arise naturally when a child brings
in something which interests from from outside
the classroom. At other times, when a child has
completed some of his teacher's questions, he
can be challenged to write some for his peers
or even for the teacher.

Since the most difficult aspect of writing assignment cards is that of devising open-ended questions, below are some comparative examples of closed and open-ended questions.

Closed.   *Count out 3 red beads and 5 green beads. How many have you altogether? Take away 4 beads. How many are left?*

Open.   *Count out 8 beads. Arrange these in patterns in more than one way. Compare your patterns with those of your partner.*

Closed.   *Find the circumference and diameter of these balls.† Draw a graph to record your results. Use your graph to find the diameter of a ball with a circumference of one yard.*

Open.   *In how many ways can you measure a ball? Can you find relationships between any of the variables you mention? (Children usually suggest: find how high it bounces; weigh it; or find its volume, circumference, or diameter. They frequently try to find relationships between weight and bounce, volume and weight, volume and circumference. Some try to find its area.)*

Closed.   *Measure the length and width of the hall giving your answers to the nearest inch.*

Open.   *Without using a ruler, find the ratio of the length to the width of the hall in as many ways as you can. Compare your results and comment on them.*

Closed.   *Find the time it takes for 20 swings of pendulums of lengths 48", 42", 36", . . ., 6". Draw a graph of your results.*

Open.   *How can you vary the swing of a pendulum? Comment on the results you obtain.*

Closed.   *A parallelogram has a base of 2.4 inches, and an area of 6 square inches. What is its height?*

Open.   *Use cardboard strips (5" and 8" long) and paper fasteners to make a parallelogram. As you change the shape, which things remain the same and which change? How many things can you vary? Investigate the relationship between the area and the height as you change the shape. Illustrate with a graph. Find the height when the area is 30 square inches. What is the shape when the area is greatest? Least? What other relationships can you discover?*

The closed question is not of great interest to children, but if it is framed in a different way so that they are challenged to think, they may become very interested in the answer. It is always a good plan to ask children to make a rough estimate before they begin to measure. Finding out how accurate their guess was motivates them to find the answer.

Assignment cards can provide a flexible approach to a program that makes provision for the different interests and abilities that exist in every classroom. The assignment cards given below were made for an initial in-service course and are, therefore, very detailed. Adults, like children, often need a gradual change from a directed to a more flexible approach.

Geo-Board

1/   *On your geo-board make all the faces and base of a triangular prism.*
2/   *Some of the faces are alike. What shape do they have?*
3/   *Count the number of sides on one triangle.*
4/   *How many sides do you have on a rectangle?*

    Students may use elastic to recreate the shapes of faces, answer the questions either orally or on paper, then check their answers.

Face Finding

I am shaped like the flat surfaces on some solids. Make solids that have faces shaped like me.

The wide use of assignment cards should be viewed as a transitional period in the development of a program that is *pupil-centered* rather than *subject-centered*. It is a firm and quite lengthy bridge between the exclusive use of a textbook and the ultimate goal of using the real life experiences of children to provide the necessary stimuli for learning.

†By this terminology we mean the circumference and diameter of a great circle of the sphere or ball.

1-7. Active Learning

In the introduction of this chapter we stated that schools should be organized, not for teachers to teach, but for children to learn. In subsequent sections a number of suggestions were made on how this might be accomplished. Utilizing children's natural curiosity to motivate their learning; incorporating the use of as many of the sensory stimuli as possible in teaching; introducing a wide variety of interesting experiences to children; and individualizing instruction are among the important ideas presented in this chapter. An approach to learning which incorporates these and other key ideas is sometimes referred to as laboratory, workshop or activity-oriented. In this book we have chosen the term *active learning*.

*Utilizing children's
natural curiosity
to motivate learning*

Chapter 2

How to Make a Start

2-1   Plans for Gradual Beginnings   19

2-2   Plans for More Complex Beginnings   21

2-3   Selecting the Best Method   23

2-4   Special Problems of Secondary Schools   23

2-5   Presentation and Content in   24
      Secondary School

There are probably as many ways to begin as there are teachers. It is important that each one should choose the approach that best suits him and the children he teaches. There is no need to wait until a large collection of equipment is made. Many teachers have found that children are anxious to help collect materials when they know what is needed. This serves a dual purpose: it helps to make the children feel that they have an important role in the development of the program and encourages them to be alert to the mathematics that is a part of their environment.

The object of this chapter is to describe as many alternatives as possible so that each teacher may choose the approach that best suits his own personality and circumstance.

These methods are ones that teachers have used successfully to implement a modern child-centered program. They range from a very gradual beginning using a small group of pupils to a "total immersion" involving the whole class in several different activities. The special problems that teachers face in secondary schools will also be considered.

2-1. Plans for Gradual Beginnings

The techniques for making a start really form a continuum, ranging from the simplest, less disruptive, one-small-group-beginning to the complex and briefly chaotic total involvement of the whole class. Teachers may choose the entry point that will accommodate their own abilities and those of the children they teach. We will describe the experiences of teachers who have used these methods, beginning with the slowest and simplest and progressing to the quicker and more complex.

Some teachers, limited by administrative restrictions or the physical aspects of the classroom, choose a simple and slow beginning. Other teachers who want to be certain of their own ability to handle a multi-group situation may also choose to begin with a small group using one period a week for student investigation of a topic. This small group may vary in size from two to eight pupils. Very often, this pilot group is made up of the better students in the class. When the size and composition of the group has been determined, the teachers plan the approach in different ways, according to their estimate of the capabilities of the pupils.

Some teachers begin with no formal direction. Materials are given to the children who are allowed to handle, play, and become familiar with them. The teachers using this plan should watch what pupils are doing with the materials and listen to what they are saying, in order to be aware of their children's interests. Oral questions or assignments can then be based on these interests.

Others structure the learning situation through the use of materials and directions. Materials can be arranged on a table in the corner of the classroom with a simple question such as "In how

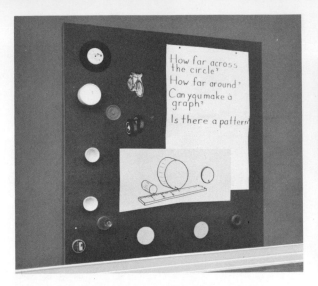

Materials arranged with simple questions

How many cubes will fit in the box?

many ways can you measure these boxes?''
or ''Find the largest box. Record how you did this.''

With younger children, the teachers could ask
informally, ''Who can find the largest box?''
This usually leads to a spirited discussion on what
is meant by ''largest'' and of ways to find out.

Many teachers prefer to begin with a more
directed lesson. One way to do this is to develop
a series of assignment or task cards. For example:

*Make a collection of rectangular boxes and blocks
of all shapes and sizes on your desk. Sort the
boxes with two square faces into a set.† In this set,
put the cubes by themselves. How are cubes
different from the other boxes in the set? Describe
the three sets you have made. In how many
different ways could you sort the whole collection
(e.g. tall, wide)?*

A series such as this will keep the group occupied
for some time and will allow the teacher to observe
their reactions and hear what they have to say.
Discussion, both with other children and with the
teacher, is of first importance at all stages. It is a
most reliable instrument for assessment and
diagnosis.

When starting with a small group, provision
must be made for the rest of the class. At the
beginning, the whole class should know what

†Our use of the word *set* is not intended to be in the strictest
mathematical sense; that is, an abstract set.

is happening and that each pupil will have his turn.
They need to be given useful work which will
occupy them while you give your attention to one
group. For example, they could be given assignments from a textbook, along with the answers,
so that they can work independently.

When you are satisfied that the plan for the
first small group is working well you will want to
involve another group. There are essentially two
ways to do this. One is to have the first return
to regular classwork while you work with a second
group. The other is to assign a new project to
the first group while introducing the initial project
to a second group.

You may also wish to extend the time allotted
for the active learning approach. As the number
of groups is increased and the amount of time
given to this way of learning is lengthened, it is
but a short step to expand the activities to include
the whole class.

Another very common plan for a gradual beginning is to set up a mathematics corner at the
back of the classroom. Frequently this consists
of a mathematical problem printed on a paper
fixed to the wall, with the necessary apparatus and
materials assembled on a table underneath. On
Monday, one row or group of students is allowed
to work at the problems, while the teacher continues to teach the rest of the class in his usual

A mathematics corner

Whole-class involvement

way. On Tuesday, a second group moves to the mathematics corner while the first returns to the regular lesson. By Friday, the whole class will have carried out the investigation at different times and an opportunity should be provided for reporting and discussion.

If the children appear to make a quick adjustment toward accepting more responsibility for their program, and the teacher feels confident of his ability to handle expansion of the activity approach, a second mathematics corner or problem centre can be set up. On Monday two rows or groups of students begin the investigations while the remainder of the class works with the teacher. On succeeding days, each group will spend two periods on the activities provided. Again, Friday should be the day for displaying the children's work and discussing their techniques, strategies and results. Since nearly half of the class has been involved in active learning at one time, it is but a small step to expand it to the whole class. This plan has the advantage of not requiring a great deal of extra work on the part of the teacher (one open-ended question lasts all one week) and, more important, it provides the children with perhaps their first opportunity to work independently of the teacher. The major disadvantage is that the teacher has little chance to observe, listen and encourage the students who are meeting the challenge of thinking for themselves in school.

2-2. Plans for more Complex Beginnings

The most complex method of beginning is that of immediate whole-class involvement. In effect, this means discarding previous or existing ways of instruction and adopting an active learning approach. Again we suggest that the class should be divided into groups. Various methods of grouping may be selected. Many teachers consider 5 or 6 students an ideal group, but some have found that the children themselves prefer to work in smaller groups — often natural friendship groups. This has the advantage of arranging children either according to their interests or according to ability. This informal, rather flexible grouping seems to work well in a variety of situations and at different age levels. There will be some individuals who like to work with different groups (and sometimes make significant contributions in several groups). Occasionally, a teacher may choose to put an able student in charge of a group. This requires careful handling; otherwise the leader will do all the work. The better students will not be challenged to use their talents if they do not work, at least some of the time, with their peers.

As with a gradual beginning there are three plans from which to choose: one of no formal direction at the start, one involving some structuring, and a plan that has step-by-step direction.

*Finding the distance across the top of the
chalkboard*

The easiest way to introduce whole-class involvement is to set aside one period a week for activity centres. Friday afternoon is a popular choice because it is usually a time when a more relaxed atmosphere prevails. The class is separated into several small groups and different mathematical problems are presented involving exploration with real materials. These assignments are usually prepared before the session and may be printed on 5" × 8" file cards. Occasionally, the teacher may present one broad question to the whole class and allow the different groups to investigate it in whatever ways they choose. The guidelines for developing good open-ended questions described earlier should be applied in this situation.

A teacher of eight-year-olds discussed with the class the problem of finding the perimeter of rectangles. The children told her the opposite sides were equal and she set each group of four to work on a different written assignment involving first estimation, then measurement of rectangles in the classroom. For example, one group measured the windows and another the chalkboard (the teacher had devised practical reasons why this measurement should be done, which satisfied the children). To the teacher's surprise, despite the initial discussion, every group measured all four sides of the rectangles to obtain the perimeter. The group measuring the chalkboard had to stand on a chair to find the distance across the top. When they had finished, the teacher asked if they could find the perimeter without standing on a chair. Eventually, a boy found out how this could be done, but to his teacher's amusement he refused to tell the others and encouraged them to think it out for themselves. By the time this measuring session was over and results were discussed, nearly all the children had found for themselves the quick method of finding the perimeter of a rectangle.

If different topics are provided for each station, it is important that they should be chosen carefully. The choice may be determined as a result of teacher-class discussion on the needs of individuals and groups. This method becomes easier as teachers gain experience working in this way and can anticipate the different problems children are likely to meet. Many teachers have progressed to the point where they are working confidently, using a variety of topics.

Some teachers like to take this opportunity of planning an integrated day. This means that the topics chosen or suggested by the children would not be confined to any one subject. For example, a topic such as travel in a foreign country would include the geography, history, art, music and the language as well as a great deal of mathematics (money equivalents, metric measures, postage rates, expense budgets, etc.). When not restricted by a rigid timetable, the interest and enthusiasm of children sustain intense effort that is very profitable in terms of the learning that takes place.

2-3. Selecting the Best Method

The following suggestions may help individual teachers to decide the point on the scale or continuum, from gradual beginning to total involvement, that will be most appropriate. If children are used to a formal classroom where they are normally restricted to working at their desks and are unaccustomed to investigating problems on their own, using available materials, they may need a period of adjustment. The older the child when he begins to think for himself and to make his own judgments, the more hesitant he may be to take full advantage of his opportunities. Children, as well as teachers, need varying amounts of time to become accustomed to this new approach to learning. Under these conditions we recommend a more gradual beginning. This type of involvement does not jeopardize the sense of security of either teacher or pupils.

The majority of those teachers who decided on more complex beginnings describe the first session as rather chaotic and hard work for them. They all agree that the children accomplished a surprising amount not only in mathematics but also in science and language. These teachers agree that they learned quite as much as the children. Some found the children reluctant to record their findings, although eager to talk about them.

In order that the more complex beginning may succeed, children will sometimes have to take responsibilities without the teacher being present (e.g. making a traffic count from the schoolyard). They will have to make decisions for themselves; which piece of equipment is most appropriate for the task, a balance scale ranging from ¼ oz. to 2 lbs., or a compression scale reading in ounces to 15 lbs.

In short, do not expect miracles. Teacher and students will need time to adjust to this way of learning.

2-4. Special Problems of Secondary Schools

Many courses in secondary schools, such as metal or wood shops, chemistry, physics, typing and home economics, often use a form of the active learning approach. That is, students in these courses are actively using materials to help them discover and understand concepts. Students' success in these classes is ample proof that this is an effective method of instruction for this age level. However, in our mathematics programs we have been reluctant to utilize this approach. Because of this reluctance, the response patterns that students have developed in mathematics classrooms are, almost without exception, adverse to the active learning approach.

The older the student, the more difficult it is to get him involved in an active way in a program that requires original and creative thinking. After all, in mathematics, we have spent years conditioning him in an atmosphere that stifled, rather than stimulated. Doing what the teacher wants and expects has been synonymous with success in school. Teachers who have participated in in-service programs can appreciate the dilemma students face when they are challenged to think for themselves.

Another problem of some significance is the great variety in levels of achievement and experience in mathematics that students possess when they arrive at secondary school. This will become more acute as a result of recent developments in the elementary schools.

The change from traditional methods of teaching to an active approach to learning is occurring at varying rates. Some students will have had extensive experience with learning through discovery, others will have had nothing but traditional teaching, and many will have had a combination of the two. The attitudes of these students to mathematics will be just as varied as their background.

The implementation of new curriculum courses in recent years has made a heavy demand on teachers to learn new content. The need to learn new ideas has had a positive effect on the teaching methods used in the classroom. The more recent our own experiences in learning, the more sympathy we have for the difficulties faced by our students. However, many teachers, pressed for time and uncertain of their new role, resort to teaching methods which allow little scope for discovery.

The problem of timetables and of organizing the program to accommodate routine and special events results in short lesson periods which do not lend themselves to practical investigations. As timetables become more flexible and special equipment is used to help structure individual programs, this problem will resolve itself.

Few secondary schools as yet have rooms designated for mathematics, so storage and availability of equipment and materials present some difficulty. No doubt, there are many other obstacles and forces that may hinder the development of techniques that will foster critical thinking. How long any of these will impede progress will be determined, in large measure, by the imagination and resourcefulness of the classroom teacher.

Immediate and long-term solutions of these problems may need to be considered separately since conditions vary so much from school to school. These problems will require patient and persistent experiment by secondary teachers. They will often need to meet their colleagues and discuss the many problems they face. The following suggestions have been discussed at various workshops:

Since students on entry will have had diverse experience, work in groups will probably be essential. A gradual introduction to active learning is advisable for those students who are new to this approach.

At the moment, some students will need experience with real materials which might in future be given in elementary schools.

Discovery learning does not always require the use of real materials. A search for pattern, for example, in arithmetic and algebra, can be made with paper and pencil.

Students require very different experiences. The availability of materials may give the ablest pupils an idea which leads to the solution of a problem; some students may not need materials at all. On the other hand, the slowest pupils may need a great deal of experience with real materials before they understand an idea or concept, or are able to solve a particular problem.

All students require some practice to fix an idea – but excessive practice is a waste of time and results in boredom.

Some teachers have succeeded in combining two 35-minute periods to give one long learning period each week.

It is worth pressing for a mathematics room where materials are readily available. Ideally; one room is needed for every full-time teacher of mathematics. If these rooms can be adjacent, not only will it be easier to share material, but part of the corridor could be used for attractive displays of students' work and visual materials.

2-5. Presentation and Content in Secondary School

Many secondary teachers feel pressure to complete the course of study, others consider that certain topics do not lend themselves to discovery methods. Discussion with colleagues from other schools often elicits suggestions for presentation which afford scope for individual or small-group investigation.

The following method has now been tried out by a number of secondary teachers. Whenever a new topic is to be studied, students are given an initial period of investigation, normally in groups of two or three. This period may or may not require real materials, depending on the topic and on the previous experience of the students. During this session, which may occupy one or two periods, many diverse problems will be raised and some discoveries will be made by the students. In future periods, the teacher should choose those problems which will lead to the development of significant mathematical ideas.

*Children taking some responsibilities in an
active learning program*

Meetings with colleagues (not only from your own school) to consider the development and presentation of specific topics will prove invaluable. Following classroom experiment, subsequent meetings will provide opportunity for students' work to be compared and discussed. This exchange of ideas will help experienced as well as inexperienced teachers.

It will also be valuable to meet with colleagues from elementary schools in order to plan some topics to cover the age range of 5 to 18. Students at secondary schools show creative ability in mathematics and science if they are given opportunities for investigation and if their imagination is captured.

A teacher of 13-year-olds had provided a variety of assignments and materials for experiments on the changing speed of objects sliding down slopes and on Galileo's experiment with free falling objects. After the first session, she encouraged the students to make their own problems and to devise experiments to solve them. They suggested a wide variety of variables which might affect the speed of objects sliding down a slope: nature of surfaces in contact (degree of roughness), area of surfaces in contact, angle of slope and length of slope. Naturally, the students needed time, but their experiments showed great originality.

Teachers of students aged 5 to 14 prepared assignments on the topic "time" for their classes and brought the resulting classroom work for exhibition and discussion. A class of 13-year-olds chose to study the history of methods of telling the time and, on their own, made a variety of working models including sundials, water clocks and sand clocks. The most interesting and complex working model was made by two girls; it comprised a pendulum and cog wheels mounted on an axle — and it worked. The whole project had absorbed the attention of older students as well as young children and had given them an added zest for mathematics and science.

A teacher of 17-year-olds had encouraged enquiry and individual research into a new topic for the group: the properties of sections of cones (ellipses, parabolas and hyperbolas). The group of students was large and individual presentations were varied and imaginative. The teacher was most encouraged by this first experience of creative learning with students of this age.

Chapter 3

Classroom Needs

3-1   Physcial Needs   29

3-2   Equipment and Materials   31

3-3   Storage   35

3-4   Books   39

3-5   Audio-Visual Aids   44

3-6   Additional Audio-Visual Aids   49

3-7   Games and Puzzles   50

If you are going to use the activity approach, even the most gradual beginning, you must give some special consideration to the arrangement of furniture and the materials in your classroom. Suggestions and lists in this chapter should help you to make this transition smoothly.

3-1. Physical Needs

When you begin with a small group (up to 8) it is still important to separate the group from the rest of the class. This not only allows the children to work with materials, but also reduces the amount of distraction for those still working individually at their desks. This separation may be achieved by arranging desks in a block (4 × 2) in a corner. If the desk tops are sloped the lids may be propped so that the working surface is horizontal. A piece of plywood or hardboard can be used to cover the whole surface if desired. Two possible arrangements of desks to create this separation are shown in the diagrams.

When you decide to have your whole class work on assignments, the room needs careful planning. There will be more room for each group to work independently if the desks are arranged in groups. Perhaps you can dispense with some of the desks. It is not always necessary that every child have one. It is often convenient to divide the classroom into sections, particularly if children are busy with different topics. Cupboards or book cases, chart stands, portable screens, etc., can

be used to partition a book corner or an experimental corner where water is being used (with a sink if possible). Desks which are not occupied can be pushed into a row along one wall and used for materials. This will leave more *free* floor space in the middle of the room.

Sometimes the corridors outside the classroom can be used for overflow activities which require more room. Experiments which involve moving objects such as balls running down slopes, long, swinging pendulums, and investigations into capacities which involve the use of water may be more conveniently done outside the classroom. In suitable weather the out-of-doors provides an ideal setting for some of this work, once the children have developed the necessary sense of responsibility.

As a beginning a school might set aside a room as a mathematics workshop or laboratory. For example, in one school the end of an auditorium was used; in another, a long narrow storeroom. Materials should be carefully labelled and stored, so that they are readily available to children and teachers. Stacking-tables can provide adequate working surfaces and chairs are unnecessary. The door may be left open when the room is in use so that the activities can spill out into the corridor.

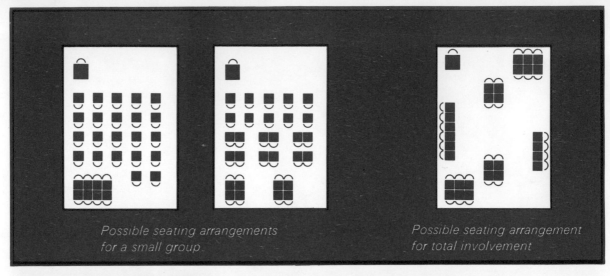

*Freedom
to
Learn*

*Possible seating arrangements
for a small group.*

*Possible seating arrangement
for total involvement*

Water activities may be done outside

Partitioning for experiment area

When mathematics laboratories are used by specialist teachers who work with more than one class, it is important that the class teacher be present to work with the children so that he can follow up the topic. Every effort should be made to integrate mathematics with other aspects of the curriculum, especially for children to the age of 11 or 12 years. When someone other than the classroom teacher is doing the teaching there is an artificial aura of difficulty established that tends to discourage children. *"If my teacher has trouble with this subject, how can they expect me to learn it?"* Arrangements with specialist teachers should be considered temporary. Otherwise, mathematics becomes a *special* subject confined to particular periods with little opportunity for sensible integration. The ultimate goal is to have every teacher both competent and confident in his own ability to provide a total program that is rich and varied enough to meet the needs of individual students. Teachers with special interests or training can provide a valuable resource for others.

The mathematics laboratory should be a *training centre* for teachers, as well as children. It is especially valuable if it is available for teacher use at regular intervals, both in and out of school hours. It can also serve as a storage depot for the more expensive equipment that cannot be provided for all classes.

3-2. Equipment and Materials

Very often the prospect of getting a larger budget to purchase more equipment is sufficiently remote to discourage teachers from getting started on a new program. A lack of funds will not seriously handicap the development of an active learning situation. The limitation will more often be the lack of imagination and initiative of individual teachers.

Some equipment, especially that normally termed *junk*, can be obtained by an appeal to children. An important consequence of this approach is that the children learn to keep their eyes open and become alert to the mathematics that abounds in the world about them. More important, this kind of participation makes mathematics real. Boxes, cans and coloured yarn belong to the wider life outside school and have a significance that transcends the classroom. Children need to be given very clear information about requirements and especially about the approximate number of objects each child should bring if the classroom is not to be swamped. (Surplus material can usually be offered to another teacher.)

The equipment required for measurement of various kinds, e.g. length, weight, time, etc., must be of good quality. Some of this can be made if a workbench with tools and materials is available

Unmarked yardsticks and foot rules in plain wood (or painted in different colours) can be cut from 1″ x ¼″ lathing. Balance scales made from one- or two-foot lengths of lath can be suspended from a cuphook and a nail or eye.

It is particularly important that scales of all kinds be easily readable. For example, to weigh light objects, scales weighing to ¼ ounce are useful, but these should have a clear dial for easy reading. This type of scale needs to be adjusted to zero before use.

Children do not necessarily need to be told how to use measuring instruments; they will often find out for themselves. If they do not do so, they may not yet be ready to use the instrument (e.g. micrometer, map measurer, or other specialized instrument). It is necessary to emphasize the special care that the more precise scientific devices require. Scales designed for weighing very light weights will not last long if misused.

Lists of Equipment and Materials

The following lists of materials and equipment should be considered as minimum for the complete implementation of an active learning program.† Few things are as frustrating, both for teachers and students, as to have an investigation curtailed because of a lack of materials. It has been our experience that all of this equipment and more, can be provided at less cost than a set of textbooks.

General. Paper: newsprint; construction, sugar or folding (various colours); gummed coloured (including 1″ squares); squared or graph paper (1″, $^1/_2$″, $^1/_4$″, $^1/_{10}$″ in large sheets); bristolboard (various colours)
Cellulose tape, coloured tape, paste, mucilage
Felt pens, powdered tempera paint, large brushes
Paper fasteners, thumb tacks, pins, scissors
Drinking straws, pipe cleaners, plasticene, coloured string
Scraps of ribbon
Coloured 1″ cubes, beads, marbles, pebbles
Dry goods: beans, rice, peas, cereal
Structural material: Unifix, Cuisenaire, Dienes' Multibase Blocks, Color-Factor

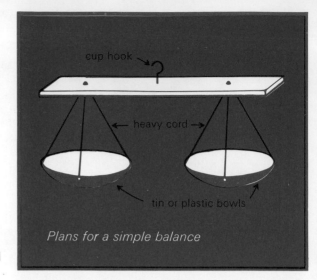

Plans for a simple balance

*Punched cardboard strips
for making two-dimensional figures*

Shapes, Volume and Capacity. Containers of all kinds in a variety of shapes and sizes: empty bottles, boxes, cardboard or plastic cups, milk or juice containers, tin cans, jam jars, etc. There should be sets of identical boxes and cylinders (plastic, cardboard or tin).
Set of balls, ranging in size from a marble to a beach ball

†A useful list of materials with sources appears in the appendix to the following:
Myron F. Rosskopf and Jerome D. Kaplan, "Educating Mathematics Specialists to Teach Children from Disadvantaged Areas," *The Arithmetic Teacher*, Vol. 15, No. 7 (November, 1968), pp. 606-612.

Scraps of patterned fabric, wallpaper
Kaleidoscopes, small rectangular mirrors
Protractors (360° if possible)
Heavy cardboard strips:
a/   5" long and ½" wide, with a hole punched
½" from each end

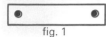

fig. 1

b/   10" long and ½" wide, with a hole punched
½" from one end and holes punched from centre
to other end at ½" intervals

fig. 2

Geo-boards: 12" squares of plywood, fibreboard
or cork, with finishing nails in various patterns,
coloured elastic bands
Measuring jugs: pint, quart, gallon, pails

Length.   12 sticks of same length: yardsticks
painted green; foot rules painted red; 2-foot rules
painted yellow; and ½-yard lengths painted orange
(all unmarked)
Popsicle sticks, spatulas, tongue depressors,
toothpicks
Yard lengths of 1" graph paper 1" wide, numbered
by the children in inches and covered with clear
plastic (fablon)
8- or 10-foot steel tape
Surveyor's chain (could be homemade of 22 yards
of string marked in one-foot intervals as well as
at each yard)
Cloth tape measures, rulers with markings at 1",
$^1/_2$", $^1/_4$", $^1/_{10}$" intervals, yardsticks
Globe, atlases, local roadmaps, topographical maps
Air line maps, fares and schedules, railway schedules
Silva compass, spirit level

Time.   Stopwatch, metronome (second hand
of classroom clock can be used, if nothing else
is available)
Egg timer
Calendars (whole year on one page is most useful)
T.V. and radio program schedules
Pendulums (can be made from plasticene, or
steel washers and string)
Toy cars and trucks
Inclined planes (The *trough* type is best for
rolling balls and marbles. A flat board with a
narrow rail or raised edge is best for rolling model
trucks and cars.)

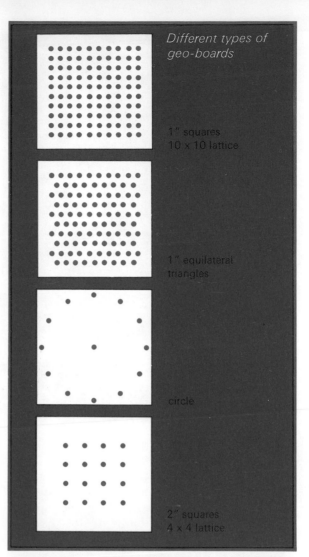

*Different types of
geo-boards*

1" squares
10 x 10 lattice

1" equilateral
triangles

circle

2" squares
4 x 4 lattice

Tracks for rolling

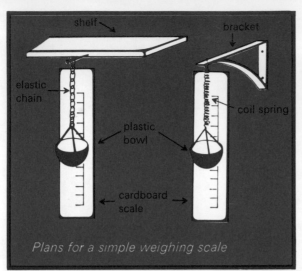

Plans for a simple weighing scale

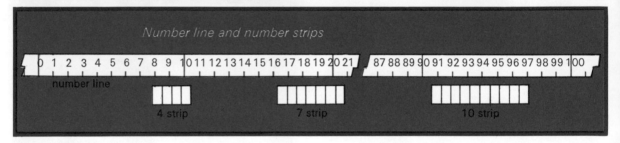

Number line and number strips

number line

4 strip   7 strip   10 strip

Weight. (Some of this equipment can be homemade.)
Balance scales (These can easily be constructed, either at home, or in the school workshop. Great variety is possible and many students like to make their own.)
Set of weights: ½ oz., 1 oz., 2 oz., 4 oz., 8 oz., 16 oz., 2 lb.
Extension scales (you can use elastic bands looped through one another or a 6″ coil spring attached to a strong paper or plastic cup. Hook this assembly over a nail driven into a shelf or a bracket. Fasten stiff white cardboard below the shelf or bracket, so that a scale can be made as equal weights are added to the cup.)
A varied collection of good scales is essential, but these could be collected gradually (and kept in a central place in the school if necessary); e.g., postal scales in ¼ oz. intervals to 4 lbs., compression scales in 1 oz. intervals to 8 lbs., extension scales in 2 oz. intervals to 25 lbs. (fish scales), bathroom scales
Stones of weights one to five pounds

Number Line. A useful number line can be made from 1″ squared paper. It should be at least 100 inches long and 2 inches wide. Cover the strip with clear plastic (fablon) to make it permanent. Short strips 1″ to 10″ long and 1″ wide can be backed with cardboard to make them stiff and then covered with plastic. This should be mounted on the classroom wall for ready reference. It can be extended beyond zero in the negative direction, when the children are ready for integers.

Miscellaneous. Your students can provide many natural objects, such as leaves, flowers, shells, stones, bulbs and seeds. Toys on wheels, wire connectors, magnets, springs (including hair rollers), parts of mechanisms such as clocks, gears and other items often classed as junk are available for the asking. These have tremendous potential for mathematics, for science, and for generating enthusiasm about learning through enquiry.

3-3. Storage

Possibly the most common complaint of teachers (if it is not the lack of materials and equipment) is the problem of where to put what they have. When you consider the addition of all the materials listed earlier, the problem does become acute. Circumstances vary widely, but lack of space suitable for storage is one of the shortcomings of most classrooms. The challenge is not only to find extra space, but to utilize efficiently that which you already have. This may be further complicated by a shortage of money for such purposes.

In this section we will outline some of the many and varied methods that teachers have used successfully in tackling the problem of storage. The basic requirements for storage units should be: *(1) materials contained must be readily available to the children, (2) available space must be efficiently used, (3) units should be mobile if possible, and (4) units should serve a variety of purposes.* The more flexible the unit, the more efficiently the classroom can be organized for active learning. Storage units may serve as display centres, room dividers, working surfaces, and so on.

The first problem is to find space. Look at your classroom. How much floor space is taken up by necessary furniture? Does every child need a desk for his exclusive use? Enough evidence has been accumulated to dispel the notion that children need the security of their own desks to work well in school. Pupils in kindergarten and in senior grades do not appear to suffer from a lack of security for want of a personal desk or chair. Even if it is not possible to dispose of any desks, much valuable floor space can be obtained by simply rearranging them.

The storage of adequate supplies of paper presents the greatest problem in most classrooms. Because of great variety in size, colour and type of paper, and the need to keep them separate, as well as conveniently placed, it is doubtful if there is any one solution appropriate for all situations. Here are some suggestions: A *paper trolley* of plywood or hardboard construction with a set of heavy duty casters provides storage, a working surface and a room divider. The dimensions will be determined by the amount and size of paper you want to store. It is more convenient to keep the

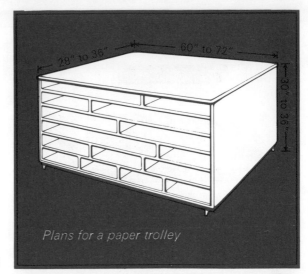

Plans for a paper trolley

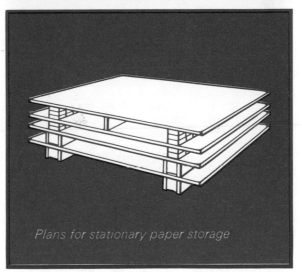

Plans for stationary paper storage

larger sheets near the top with the lower compartments reserved for the smaller pieces. The partitions should be spaced so that there is plenty of room to get paper in and out and still keep it in good order. If you have a choice between one large trolley and two small ones, choose the two smaller, since they will be lighter, easier to move, and will add to the versatility of your classroom organization.

Cheaper and somewhat less convenient storage can be provided with some cinder blocks, breeze blocks or bricks, and plywood or boards. Choose

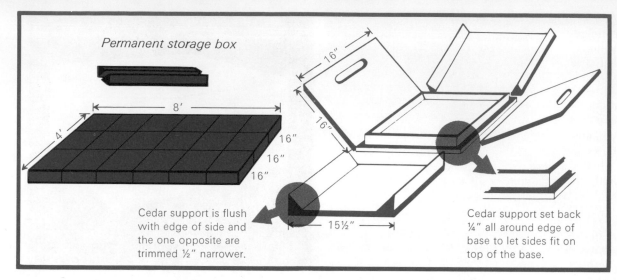

Permanent storage box

8'

4'

16"

16"

16"

16"

16"

16"

15½"

Cedar support is flush
with edge of side and
the one opposite are
trimmed ½" narrower.

Cedar support set back
¼" all around edge of
base to let sides fit on
top of the base.

your location carefully, since this storage unit
cannot be moved without dismantling. It should
have one end against a wall to improve its stability.
Variety in shelf heights can be achieved through
choice of cinder blocks (6", 8" or 10" in height, or
the use of 2" bricks). The shelves should be cut
from smooth plywood so that they are all in one
piece. Planks or boards one inch thick and eight
or ten inches wide can be used instead of plywood;
however, these tend to be uneven and make it
difficult to slide paper in and out, so that the whole
unit is somewhat less stable. The top must be solid
and smooth if it is to be a working surface. A coat of
paint will improve its appearance and utility.
Contact paper in bright colours and patterns with
a plasticized surface is even better.

The smaller sizes of paper in relatively small
quantities can be hung from a wire line or a rod
using coat hangers and clothes pins, pegs or spring
clamps. This arrangement must be set at a height
within easy reach of the children and away from
traffic routes. It is difficult to remove one sheet at a
time, and some smooth-surfaced papers do not
hang well. The very large sheets may be kept in a
loose roll tied with string, but this usually produces
a *set* in the paper that makes it difficult to use.
This can be partially overcome by spreading it out
over heat before it is to be used or by rolling it in the
opposite way.

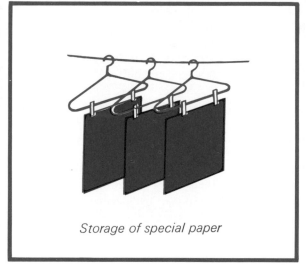

Storage of special paper

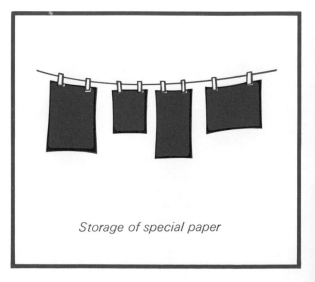

Storage of special paper

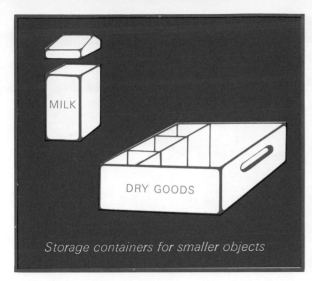

Storage containers for smaller objects

Materials other than paper and the various pieces of equipment can be stored in a variety of ways. Perhaps the most orderly and yet flexible method is to use a set of bins or boxes which are easily made from ¼" plywood. Two different sizes are the most suitable for storage and economical in terms of material. Two 4' × 8' sheets of plywood will make three 16" × 16" × 16" boxes, and seven 16" × 16" × 8" trays. You may find other combinations that are more appropriate for your classroom.

Some lengths of 2" × 2" cedar cut down the diagonal are available from lumber dealers and can be used to make the boxes virtually indestructible. All joints should be both nailed (1" finishing nails) and glued. Lids can be added if you feel they are necessary. Paint each face a different colour and you will have both a functional and an attractive storage unit. It can be used to hold smaller containers of plasticene, sand, cereal, beans, pipe cleaners, paper straws and so on. Milk cartons in one- two- and three-quart sizes can be cut to fit into the shallow boxes. They make ideal compartments for small objects.

The bins or boxes may be stacked or arranged in any order. They are ideal for transporting materials when they have to be shared with other classrooms. Commercially produced stacking storage units are available in many sizes. These are usually made from heavy galvanized wire welded

to form a deep tray. They are designed to fit together securely in a stack. Costs vary greatly, not only according to size, but also because of the different materials used. Sometimes it is possible to obtain from commercial companies containers that are no longer useful because of changes in the size of products or procedures in handling them. New units are expensive, but surplus or obsolete ones can be purchased very reasonably.

Rectangular dish pans made from plastic are both colourful and useful. They do not stack as securely as the trays mentioned earlier, but they can be used for a variety of purposes besides storage. Corrugated cardboard boxes that are reasonably sturdy can serve as storage units. Cut off the top flaps and make certain that the bottom is securely glued or stapled. Scraps or pieces of vinyl-coated wallpaper will make these boxes stronger and quite attractive. Carrying handles or hand grips can be cut in the ends to facilitate transporting them. Wooden six-quart baskets can be collected in sufficient quantity to use for storage. Painted in bright colours and arranged on shelves that are within reach of the children, they provide an economical and reasonably functional means of keeping materials.

Every bin, box, tray, carton, jar or bottle must be labelled. In the case of larger storage units, a list of the apparatus or materials they contain should be fixed to one face of the box. Your children can be of great assistance in organizing a system for storing equipment. Since they will be using it almost

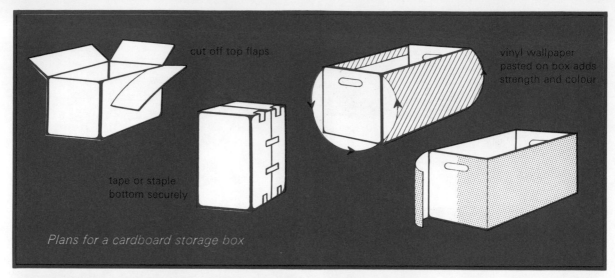

cut off top flaps

tape or staple
bottom securely

vinyl wallpaper
pasted on box adds
strength and colour

Plans for a cardboard storage box

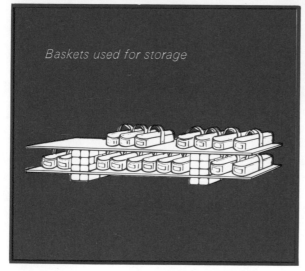

Baskets used for storage

constantly and will be expected to keep it in good order, their participation in the planning promotes responsibility for using it sensibly and keeping everything in its proper place. When apparatus and materials are readily available, children will often tackle problems in unexpected ways. For example, if balance scales are close at hand, they will often think of weighing as a solution to problems such as "which holds most?" or "which is the largest?" It is extremely worthwhile to stimulate this kind of originality in children. A wealth of material attractively stored and readily available will make it possible.

3-4. Books

Teachers who have been accustomed to relying on textbooks for their programs may find it difficult at first to adjust to a situation where a single text does not dominate the work. Of course, textbooks will still be a necessary element in the classroom. They will be a prime resource for ideas, methods, facts, exercises, etc. In order to accomplish this role, it will be necessary to break away from the singly adopted text and in its place, have available several textbooks as well as many other supplementary materials. In this new classroom situation where children's natural curiosity is being stimulated, textbooks will, indeed, enjoy an even wider role.

We suggest that the classroom and staffroom libraries should include

1/ *Reference books, in mathematics as well as in other subjects. Most pupils, including some young children, prefer a selection of adult reference books, and not those originally written for children (usually written down to children). Reference books, especially keys for identifying animals, birds, flowers, shapes, crystals, etc., need to be well illustrated and in good variety.*

2/ *Background books that suggest there may be different ideas or different points of view in mathematics as well as in other subjects. Pupils need to be given opportunities to evaluate and reconcile other viewpoints than their own.*

3/ *Source books that provide ideas for pupils and teachers. Booklets on specific topics (including books written initially as texts) suggest many useful starting points for investigations.*

It is suggested that every teacher should build up a classroom library containing as varied and attractive a collection as possible of these books. This would be in addition to those in the central library or resource centre. If your children are not used to reading mathematics books for pleasure you will need to find ways of attracting their attention to individual books. For example, you might ask a question and send them to a specific book for the answer.

Unfortunately, even some of the books in the list we recommend give an answer instead of asking a further question which will make the child think for himself. However, once pupils are accustomed to discovery learning, they become critical of the statements they read in books, as the following example shows. After the children had watched a snail give birth to a baby snail, several of them wrote graphic accounts of the incident. One boy concluded:

"Mrs. Cook said snails lay eggs. The books said so to. We had to say 'This one didnot.' We saw it being born, And it came out of its mothers tummy, I believe my eyes!"

Some ten-year-olds read that a man needs one-fiftieth of his weight in food every day and that a mouse needs to eat half its weight in food in order to stay alive. They challenged this statement. It was easy enough to conduct an experiment on the pet mice in the classroom and observations were carried out over a period of two weeks. It was more difficult to persuade one of the fathers to weigh the food he ate, but eventually this too was achieved. The statement in the book led to some interesting experiments devised by the children themselves. Worthwhile practice in arithmetic skills was a natural consequence of the activity.

Teachers, too, will find many books to help them when they are at a loss for ideas, or need help in the development of their work. The biggest difficulty for the busy teacher is to find time to review and select the books, pamphlets and magazines that will be most useful. Limited budgets for library purposes make it all the more important to get the best value for your money. The following list contains those books that we have found most useful in our work with teachers and children. There are many others that could be included and additional titles are being published regularly, so that it is extremely difficult to keep up to date on the best books available. Book lists are much like women's hats — they are out of style as soon as a new model appears. It is with these limitations in mind that we offer these suggestions.

Books on Teaching Methods

Grossnickle, Foster E., and others, *Discovering Meanings in Elementary School Mathematics.* 1968.

New York, Holt, Rinehart & Winston, Inc.

Howard, Charles, and Dumas, E., *Basic Procedures in Teaching Arithmetic.* 1963.

Boston, Raytheon Education Co., D. C. Heath & Co.

Marks, John L., and others, *Teaching Elementary School Mathematics for Understanding,* 2d ed. 1967.

New York, McGraw-Hill Book Co.

Ministry of Education, *Primary Education: Suggestions for the Consideration of Teachers and Others.* 1959.

London, Her Majesty's Stationery Office.

Sealey, L. G. W., and Gibbon, V., *Communication and Learning in the Primary School,* rev. ed. 1963.

Toronto, The Copp Clark Publishing Company.
Oxford, Blackwell.
New York, Humanities Press, Inc.

Books on the Teaching of Mathematics

Bailey, C. A. R., and others, *Contemporary School Mathematics,* St. Dunstan's College Booklets
Sets and Logic
Computers
Matrices
Shape, Size and Place
An Introduction to Probability and Statistics. 1964.

London, Edward Arnold & Co.

Dienes, Z. P., *Building Up Mathematics.* 1960.

Don Mills, Ontario, J. M. Dent and Sons (Canada) Ltd.
London, Hutchinson Educational, Ltd.
New York, Humanities Press, Inc.

Fehr, Howard F., and Phillips, Jo McKeeby, *Teaching Modern Mathematics in the Elementary School.* 1967.

Don Mills, Ontario, Addison-Wesley (Canada) Ltd.
London, Addison-Wesley Publishing Co.
Reading, Mass., Addison-Wesley Publishing Co., Inc.

Ohmer, Merlin M., *Elementary Geometry for Teachers.* 1969.

Don Mills, Ontario, Addison-Wesley (Canada) Ltd.
London, Addison-Wesley Publishing Company.
Reading, Mass., Addison-Wesley Publishing Co., Inc.

Peterson, John A., and Hashisaki, J., *Theory of Arithmetic,* 2d ed. 1967.

Rexdale, Ontario, John Wiley & Sons (Canada).
New York, John Wiley & Sons, Inc.

Schools Council, *Mathematics in Primary Schools,* Curriculum Bulletin No. 1. 1965.

Toronto, British Information Service.
London, Her Majesty's Stationery Office.

Sealey, L. G. W., *The Creative Use of Mathematics in the Junior School,* rev. ed. 1965.	Toronto, The Copp Clark Publishing Company. Oxford, Blackwell. New York, Humanities Press, Inc.
Webber, G. Cuthbert, *Mathematics for Elementary Teachers.* 1967.	Don Mills, Ontario, Addison-Wesley (Canada) Ltd. London, Addison-Wesley Publishing Company. Reading, Mass., Addison-Wesley Publishing Co., Inc.
Willerding, Margaret, *Elementary Mathematics: Its Structures and Concepts,* 1966.	New York, John Wiley & Sons, Inc.

Books for Classroom Library

Adler, Clair F., *Modern Geometry.* 1958.	New York, McGraw-Hill Book Co.
Adler, Irving, *The Giant Golden Book of Mathematics.* 1960.	New York, Golden Press, Inc.
Brumfiel, Charles F., and Krause, Eugene, *Elementary Mathematics for Teachers.* 1969.	Don Mills, Ontario, Addison-Wesley (Canada) Ltd. London, Addison-Wesley Publishing Company. Reading, Mass., Addison-Wesley Publishing Co., Inc.
Bryne, John R., *Modern Elementary Mathematics.* 1966.	Maidenhead, Berks, McGraw-Hill Publishing Co., Ltd. New York, McGraw-Hill Book Co.
Coxeter, H. S. M., *Introduction to Geometry.* 1961.	New York, John Wiley & Sons, Inc.
Elliott, H. A., and others, *Working With Geometry,* Books 1 and 2. *Working With Mathematics,* Books 3, 4, and 5. 1968.	Toronto, Holt, Rinehart and Winston of Canada, Ltd.
Elliott, H. A., and others, *Geometry in the Classroom: New Concepts and Methods.* 1968.	Toronto, Holt, Rinehart and Winston of Canada, Ltd.
Hogben, L., *Man Must Measure: The Wonderful World of Mathematics.* 1955.	London, Macdonald & Co. New York, Doubleday & Co., Inc.
Johnson, Donovan and Glenn, W. H., *Exploring Mathematics Series,* Books 1-12. 1960.	Scarborough, Ontario, McGraw-Hill Company of Canada, Ltd. London, Murray Publishers. New York, McGraw-Hill Book Co.
Keedy, Mervin L., *A Modern Introduction to Basic Mathematics,* 2d ed. 1969.	Don Mills, Ontario, Addison-Wesley (Canada) Ltd. London, Addison-Wesley Publishing Co. Reading, Mass., Addison-Wesley Publishing Co., Inc.
Keedy, Mervin L., *Number Systems,* 2d ed. 1969.	Don Mills, Ontario, Addison-Wesley (Canada) Ltd. London, Addison-Wesley Publishing Co. Reading, Mass., Addison-Wesley Publishing Co., Inc.

McWhirter, Ross and Norris, *Guinness Book of World Records,* rev. ed. 1968.	Don Mills, Ontario, Saunders of Toronto, Ltd. New York, Sterling Publishing Co., Inc.
Moss, G. A., *Think of a Number,* Books 1 and 2 and Teacher's Notes. 1958.	Oxford, Blackwell.
Nuffield Junior Science Project – Teacher's Guides I & II, *Apparatus: A Source Book of Information and Ideas, Animals and Plants: A Source Book of Information and Ideas,* Background Series: *Autumn Into Winter, Mammals in Classrooms, Science and History.* 1967.	Don Mills, Ontario, Science Research Assoc. (Canada) Ltd. London, William Collins, Sons & Co., Ltd. Chicago, Science Research Associates.
Nuffield Mathematics Teaching Project – Teacher's Guides, *I Do and I Understand, Pictorial Representation, Beginnings I, Shape and Size I, Computation and Structure I,* (Others to follow). 1967.	Don Mills, Ontario, Longmans Canada, Ltd. London, W & R Chambers and John Murray. New York, John Wiley & Sons, Inc.
Ravielli, A., *Adventures With Shapes.* 1960.	London, Phoenix House Publications.
Razzell, A. G., and Watts, K. G. O., *Mathematical Topics,* Books 1-12. 1964.	London, Hart-Davis, Rupert, Ltd.
Razzell, A. G., and Watts, K. G. O., *Probability: The Science of Chance, This Is 4: The Idea of a Number.* 1965.	New York, Doubleday & Co., Inc.
Ringenberg, Lawrence A., *Informal Geometry.* 1967.	New York, John Wiley & Sons, Inc.
Smart, James R., *Introductory Geometry: An Informal Approach.* 1967.	Grange-Over-Sands, Lancashire, Wadsworth (J.) Ltd. Belmont, Calif., (Brooks/Cole), Wadsworth Publishing Co., Inc.
Webber, G. Cuthbert and Brown, John A., *Basic Concepts of Mathematics,* 2d ed. 1969.	Don Mills, Ontario, Addison-Wesley (Canada) Ltd. London, Addison-Wesley Publishing Co. Reading, Mass., Addison-Wesley Publishing Co., Inc.
Weyl, P. K., *Men, Ants and Elephants.* 1961.	Toronto, The MacMillan Company of Canada. London, Phoenix House Publications. New York, Viking Press, Inc.
Whittaker, D. E., *Pathway to Mathematics,* Mathematics through Discovery Books, 1-3 and Teacher's Book. 1965.	London, Harrap.

General Mathematics Background

Association of Teachers of Mathematics, *Notes on Mathematics in Primary Schools.* 1967.	London, Cambridge University Press. New York, Cambridge University Press.

Cundy, H. M., and Rollett, A. P., *Mathematics Models*, 2d ed. 1961.	London, Oxford University Press. New York, Oxford University Press.
Davis, Robert, *Discovery in Mathematics: A Text for Teachers*. 1964.	Don Mills, Ontario, Addison-Wesley (Canada) Ltd. London, Addison-Wesley Publishing Co. Menlo Park, California, Addison-Wesley Publishing Co., Inc.
Davis, Robert, *Explorations in Mathematics: A Text for Teachers*. 1966.	Don Mills, Ontario, Addison-Wesley (Canada) Ltd. London, Addison-Wesley Publishing Co. Menlo Park, California, Addison-Wesley Publishing Co., Inc.
Elliott, H. A., *Numbers, Shapes and Patterns*. 1968.	Toronto, Holt, Rinehart and Winston of Canada, Ltd.
Fletcher, T. J., *Some Lessons in Mathematics*. 1964.	London, Cambridge University Press. New York, Cambridge University Press.
Land, F. W., *The Language of Mathematics*. 1963.	Toronto, Doubleday Publishers. London, Murray Publishers. New York, Doubleday & Co., Inc.
Paling, D., and Fox, J., *Elementary Mathematics – A Modern Approach I and II*. 1966.	London, Oxford University Press. New York, Oxford University Press.
Sawyer, W. W., *Mathematician's Delight*. 1943.	London, Penguin. Baltimore, Penguin Books, Inc.
Sawyer, W. W., *Prelude to Mathematics*. 1955.	London, Penguin. Baltimore, Penguin Books, Inc.
Sawyer, W. W., *Vision in Elementary Mathematics*. 1955.	London, Penguin. Baltimore, Penguin Books, Inc.

Magazines and Bulletins

The National Council of Teachers of Mathematics, *The Arithmetic Teacher* (Elementary Schools).	Washington, D.C., N.C.T.M., 1201-16th Street, N.W.
The National Council of Teachers of Mathematics, *The Mathematics Teacher* (Secondary Schools).	Washington, D.C., N.C.T.M., 1201-16th Street, N.W.
Association of Teachers of Mathematics, *Mathematics Teaching*.	Lancashire, England, Chambers, Nelson.

As with materials and apparatus, it is important for the classroom library to be planned so that the children find it easy to use. Whether your collection ranges from a few books to several hundred, the enthusiasm and skill with which children seek out both reference and recreational reading materials will depend in large measure on the way you use books yourself and on how you make them available to your pupils. It is a talent well worth developing.

3-5. Audio-Visual Aids

Schools are often described as reflections of the society they serve — usually with a fifty-year time lag! Nowhere is this criticism more appropriate than in our use of modern technology in communication. We have been rather firmly shackled by our complete faith in the power of the written (or printed) word. Our instructional techniques have been shaped to a large degree by the unique, linear, line-at-a-time characteristics of print. The child of today, with so much out-of-school experience with television and films, finds it difficult to adjust the fast paced existence of his world to the slow, point-after-point pace of the school. Teachers of very young children have been amazed at the tremendous range of experience and the intense curiosity their students bring to school. We must harness this natural curiosity to the business of education and we must do it far more efficiently and effectively than we have ever done before. Our society has provided the tools — projectors, films, tape recorders, record players, television, and so on. We must learn how to use them. Current developments in curriculum demand that every learner has the opportunity to proceed at a pace consistent with his interests and abilities. With the emphasis shifting from teaching to learning and from the *teacher* to *one-who-makes-it-possible-for-others-to-learn,* it is essential that materials be made available to pupils in all appropriate settings: in classrooms, in libraries, in resource centres, in laboratories and at home. Not only must the materials be available, but opportunities to use them must be provided along with the necessary encouragement and advice. Remember, the teacher himself can be considered an *audio-visual aid of the first order.* Careful integration of all aids to learning into the mainstream of education will enable our schools to come closer to the needs of the children of today. John Dewey aptly expressed this idea when he said, "Children are people. They grow into tomorrow only as they live today."

It is not the purpose of this book to outline in detail the possible uses of audio-visual materials in the classroom. Many excellent publications already exist which contain a wealth of suggestions and specific recommendations as to types of projectors and other equipment. We will describe those aids which have been found most useful in supporting teachers' work and stimulating children to thinking in an active, creative way. Naturally, it is impossible to include all the equipment and materials that could be used since there is much that we have not yet seen and there are new items being added every day.

16 mm. Films†

It is important that films be carefully selected for the purpose you have in mind and then shown at the right time. For example, unless teachers (or parents) are well acquainted with the aims of active learning, the films listed below may do more harm than good. It is also important for the viewing audience to know the teachers and children shown in the film had had some years of experience with these learning methods when the films were made. (Some teachers become discouraged when they first begin because their classrooms seem chaotic, whereas there is no hint of this in the films.) The films were made because it is rarely possible to give teachers participating in a workshop an opportunity to see children learning by discovery methods. The next best experience is to see it on film.

I Do and I Understand is a 15 minute, black and white film made by the British Petroleum Company for the Nuffield Mathematics Teaching Project. It shows a class of nine-year-olds in a traditional school in Britain working in a mathematics laboratory on assignment cards made by the teacher. The film portrays some of the initial developments in Britain and is somewhat restricted in scope.

Maths Alive is a 30 minute colour film showing children of ages 5 to 11 years in four British schools working on mathematical assignments. One rural school and three urban schools are represented. Because the film aimed at showing small groups of children devising experiments to help them to solve problems new to them, viewers are not aware of the large classes working in the background.

†These films can be obtained through the following sources: Canada: Learning Materials Service Unit, Dept. of Education, 559 Jarvis St., Toronto 5, Ontario. England: B.B.C. Television Centre, Wood Lane, London W 12. United States: B.B.C., 630 Fifth Ave., New York, 10020.

*Availability of projectors will encourage
students to use films*

Except for the rural school, the smallest class contained 40 children. The film moves rapidly from one incident to another in an attempt to give a representative sample of assignments both oral and written. Part of the commentary was made by asking the children to discuss what they had done as soon as they had completed the assignment. John Howard of the Lincoln College of Education has succeeded in capturing the natural reactions of children to active learning situations. Rarely does the obviously *acted* sequence intrude on what appears to be a normal classroom performance.

Maths is a Monster is one of a series of five films on *Discovery and Experience* made by the British Broadcasting Corporation. It is a black and white film, which runs for 30 minutes. Mrs. Dora Whittaker, Mathematics Advisor to the City of Nottingham, England, is shown working with children of ages 7 to 11 years. As an advisor, Mrs. Whittaker worked in different schools with each teacher in turn, using the particular teaching strength of the individual teacher to begin discovery techniques. In one classroom, the emphasis is on biology, in another, the planets, and in another, English. An attempt is made to show the progression of certain topics (e.g. area and geometric shapes) as the film moves from one age group to another. The commentary emphasizes the value of an integrated approach to learning.

Into Tomorrow is a 30 minute black and white film photographed for the Nuffield Junior Science Project by John Howard. It shows a class of nine-year-olds in Britain on an expedition in their city environment. The questions they ask and the experiments they devise in order to find the answers arise naturally from this experience. Many of the problems require a mathematical investigation or calculation for their solution. This film not only shows the philosophy and advantages of active learning but also the integration of disciplines.

Nuffield Mathematics Teaching Project is illustrated in a series of five 30 minute black and white B.B.C. films made at the request of the organizer of the project, Dr. Geoffrey Matthews. Of particular interest is the fourth of the series, called *Checking Up.* It shows a member of the Piaget Institute in Geneva administering individual check-ups to determine the child's grasp of a particular concept. The problem of assessment and evaluation is discussed at some length.

Single Concept 8 mm. Film Loops

These have been developed to incorporate many of the advantages of movies in an inexpensive, remarkably simple projection technique that uses film cartridges. Loading and unloading is a matter of seconds and the film can be stopped, started and repeated without a hand touching the film. The cartridge-projector and rear view screen is compact, mobile and easy to operate. It is ideal for use with small groups within the classroom because it does not require light control or blackout.

While the difficulties of projecting are reduced to a minimum, the real value to the program is determined by the choice of films. Many titles are presently available and more films are being produced every month. Only those that support and enrich your program should be made available to your children. You are the only one who can make the selection after thoughtful, unhurried previewing.

35 mm. Filmstrips

Rolls of still pictures designed to be projected successively with the text printed on the film, or with a sound recording on an accompanying disc, have been used in classrooms for many years. The general practice of using films or filmstrips in special rooms with elaborate equipment determined not only when and how frequently this medium was used, but also how many children were in the audience (often more than one class). To be effective, the filmstrips must be available for viewing in the classroom at a time appropriate to the needs of a single child or a small group of children. The projectors should be simple enough for young children to operate without damaging films and of sufficient wattage to use without light control or blackout.

Again, the selection of filmstrips is vital to the contribution these aids can make to the total program. There is an unfortunate tendency on the part of producers to make each strip *tell* as much as it can. Telling and teaching seem synonomous in their minds; therefore, the filmstrip tends to assume a teaching function that is alien to the discovery approach. Fortunately, children themselves can adapt and invent ways of using the filmstrips to suit their own purposes. Investigations on topics such as shape and size can be carried out using filmstrips originally prepared for other subjects, such as science, geography and art. The more practice children have in relating the mathematics they are learning to everyday experience, the more alert they are to the mathematical possibilities in their environment. This not only improves their mathematics, but helps them to develop creative, versatile and thinking minds.

2" × 2" Slides

The use of black and white or coloured 35 mm. film to record the significant experiences of both adults and children has become very popular in our society. Unfortunately, the in-school use of slides has not even begun to keep pace with their wide-spread application in the home and in industry. For some reason teachers and others can enjoy and profit from an evening viewing coloured slides at home, or in an auditorium, yet it is not a *respectable* activity in school. Happily, there are signs that this reluctance is diminishing, especially for subjects other than mathematics.

Few visual aids are as flexible or as closely tied to the classroom program as a collection of slides illustrating pupils' work and specific situations that have relevance to the topic being studied. They are especially useful for investigations of symmetry, similarity and congruence. They provide ready examples for students of pattern and structure in the real world. Best of all, they can record the stages of development of children in a way that stimulates a best effort and provides an immensely valuable resource in interpreting the school program to parents and others.

Overhead Projectors

Recent improvements have made these machines much more useable in classrooms at all levels. They are portable, much less expensive, and have a wide range of accessories that permit greater flexibility in visual presentations than was possible before. It takes time for teachers to become confident in using them. They are not an adequate substitute for the blackboard and were never intended to be. When used with good judgment and reasonable skill, this type of projector makes possible many types of visual presentation that cannot be provided by any other machine. The advantages of the overhead projector are the simplicity of operation, no blackout of the room, the possibility of projecting on any flat surface, and the *operator* stands or sits in front of the children, not behind. These advantages make this machine a worthwhile addition to your stock of aids for learning whether used for presentations to the whole class, to small groups, or by the children themselves.

Television

It would be difficult to explore fully here the possibilities for extending and enriching the back-ground of experience for all children with this medium of communication. Educational television has taken many long steps forward in recent years. Many enthusiasts have even suggested that it could profitably replace the teacher in certain situations. The future of television in the class-room will largely depend on how the professional teacher reacts and utilizes this powerful instrument for communication. If it is treated as another aid to learning and used with discretion to do the things it does best, then the pupils and the teacher will benefit greatly. On the other hand, if it is rejected, ignored, or relied upon without critical analysis of every program, the machine may well assume the dominant role because the teacher has not accepted the responsibilities demanded of a professional.

To a large extent, the use of television will depend on how much the classroom resembles a learning laboratory where the children are actively engaged in investigations of all kinds at different levels of sophistication. At the moment, televised programs do not really accommodate wide ranges of ability or interest and the student is placed in the passive role of sitting and watching others. There is little flexibility either in viewing times or choice of programs. When (and the time may not be far away) a teacher can preview programs to determine their usefulness, choose one to be shown at a time convenient to the classroom program (and repeated if desired), educational television will become a significant

aid to learning in the classroom. It would be more desirable to have the teacher participate in the development of television lessons, or at least give suggestions and ideas to those in charge of the program.

Tape Recorders

The use of sound recording devices has challenged many children and teachers to undertake some very stimulating and creative activities in the classroom. New machines are compact, portable and almost foolproof in their operation. Children use them to record their discussions, develop radio plays (with sound effects), improve reading and listening skills, interview classroom visitors, prepare their own current events broadcasts, develop their own *programmed* materials in history, mathematics, etc. and to record their musical or dramatic presentations. Teachers find them useful for assessing individual progress in reading, language and arithmetical computation (by getting a child to explain his method). Directions for certain activities can be recorded in advance, thus freeing the teacher to provide individual help and guidance when it is needed. Sets of head phones increase the versatility of this equipment immensely and permit individual or small group instruction without distracting others. Children are fascinated by the sound of their own voices and a tape recorder tends to stimulate them to even greater efforts in their work.

3-6. Additional Audio-Visual Aids

While some of the audio-visual aids that have been described already may seem beyond the reach of many teachers, because of economic reasons or prejudice (indeed, some have called them *peripheral gadgetry*), the items included here have long been considered essential to good classroom instruction. The models, charts and pictures provided the *visual* aid, while the teacher looked after the *audio* aspect of the presentation. The purpose of this section is not to recommend a long list of these visual aids, but to suggest some different ways of using them in the classroom.

The essence of the modern approach to mathematics is the increased involvement of the pupil in his mathematics, his freedom to investigate in his own way, and the stimulation of his interest through the provision of a wide variety of materials and equipment. While sufficient materials and apparatus are vital to this approach, the most influential of all aids to learning is the *teacher*. It is easy to hold up a geometric model and talk about it. It is not so easy to step back and allow the students to examine, handle, discuss and think about the possibilities inherent in the material. Initially, this appears to be a waste of valuable time. There is an almost overwhelming urge to step in, tell them what they are looking for, show them how, and then get on with some practice. This attitude has been formed by our own school experience, our professional training, and a number of years of classroom practice. It is not easy to overcome. It is doubly difficult when you are pioneering the new approach and lack the support of many of your colleagues. Your greatest reinforcement will come from your students as they develop confidence in themselves and become enthusiastic about learning in this way.

There are a few basic guidelines that should be applied to the selection of learning aids. They must be materials that children can use rather than objects designed for demonstration purposes. Obviously, they need to be fairly simple while, at the same time, attractive and reasonably durable. Most important, they should assist children to reach a level of understanding that will eventually allow them to dispense with the aids altogether.

In the beginning, it is much better to use materials that are readily available, rather than the more expensive commercial products. There is an important consequence to this approach: the children learn to keep their eyes open and can soon identify the mathematical possibilities in common materials. This kind of mathematics is *real*. As mentioned earlier, cardboard boxes, plastic jars, pebbles and coloured yarn belong to the wider life outside the school and have a significance that travels beyond the classroom. Finally, this material is inexpensive and permits an immediate start on developing an activity-centered classroom.

Commercial materials, such as Cuisenaire rods, Dienes' multibase blocks, Unifix, Color-Factor, etc., are useful and merit serious consideration in selecting equipment for your classroom. The important decision is whether such material will improve and enrich your program, or whether you will adopt the program written for the material. It is wise to sample different materials with different children at various stages. Certainly, not all children will need them at the same time. Variety in material also helps to focus attention on the fundamental mathematics involved and minimizes the danger of attaching too much significance to the material.

Geometric models are just as essential to the development of ideas concerning space and shape, as are sticks, beads and bottle caps to the formation of number concepts. Since the study of geometry has only recently been introduced in the elementary school, and from a completely different viewpoint than that of the traditional secondary school program, it is important that suitable experiences should be provided for the children. Appropriate materials are vital. The first stage is to collect boxes of all shapes and sizes, cylindrical containers, balls, cones, etc. Early investigations of shape and size can be carried out using familiar, everyday materials. Commercial sets of models are most useful when more complex shapes are being considered and when early intuitive ideas about cubes, cuboids and cylinders are being expanded Ideally, these models should be small enough to be handled easily and their dimensions scaled in such a way as to facilitate comparison of volumes, surface area and other properties.

The most useful charts are those developed by the children themselves. Displays of commercially prepared diagrams are of questionable value, since they accomplish little except to provide a quick reference for terms and definitions. Children need to be encouraged to make their graphs, diagrams and other mathematical representations of the results of their investigations as attractive as possible. Displays of pupils' work in the class-room and in corridors serve a dual purpose: they motivate thoughtful work on the part of the students and they inform others about the work being done. There will be no lack of material from which to choose, and the demand for display space will eliminate those *well-worn* exhibitions which appear year after year and remain for weeks at a time. Few things reveal dull, unimaginative teaching as quickly as the absence of recently completed pupils' work on the bulletin boards of the classroom.

3-7. Games and Puzzles

Not long ago, after hearing a presentation on the use of games in a mathematics program, a teacher commented, "That's very interesting and sounds like fun, but when are you going to teach them how to work?" It is curious that many people (teachers included) still link work to drudgery and discomfort, while anything that provides pleasure must be recreational. To learn you must work; working is unpleasant; therefore learning must involve drudgery and discomfort. Small wonder that so many people develop an early and abiding dislike for mathematics.

Games are fun. They are intended to be. They are also tremendously useful devices for developing skill in mathematics. Practice in computational skills is just as effective and much more palatable when disguised in a game context. Students devise and sharpen strategies of various kinds when confronted with problems that require advance planning involving the anticipated moves of their opponents. It is regrettable that card games, games with dice, number games; in fact most games have been considered unsuitable for classroom use. Many teachers would hesitate a long time before allowing students to flip coins or toss dice in an investigation of probability. Social taboos have inhibited worthwhile research many times in the past. Perhaps our enlightened society will encourage the injection of some fun and excitement into the serious business of education.

Mathematical games should be introduced when your pupils are ready for them. For example, if children are given a game like *Snakes and Ladders* to play before they know their simple addition facts, they will count in ones and achieve no useful purpose. When encouraged to calculate

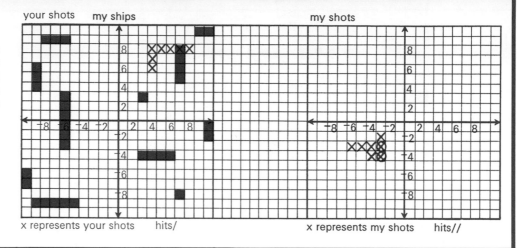

Battleship

Battleship	
1—aircraft carrier	6 spaces
1—battleship	5 spaces
2—cruisers	4 spaces
2—destroyers	3 spaces
3—submarines	2 spaces
2—P.T. boats	1 space

your shots   my ships   my shots

x represents your shots   hits/   x represents my shots   hits//

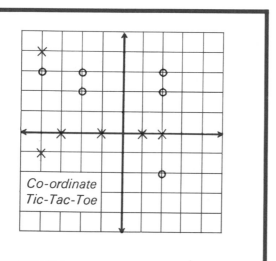

Co-ordinate Tic-Tac-Toe

the number to which they should move without counting in ones, children are having worthwhile practice in addition without being aware of this. In a similar way, a game like *Lotto*, in which attention has been focussed on the four operations (e.g. 9×4, $48 \div 6$, $19 + 8$, $33 - 9$), may provide the necessary stimulus, if provided at a time when two children need an incentive to make an effort to memorize these facts.

There are useful games for later stages too. For example, there is more than one variety of *battleship*, a game providing practice in the use of co-ordinates. Each of two players has one pair of axes; the axes for one player are shown in the figure. Each player marks in eleven ships of agreed length on one of the graphs. In turn, each player fires *shots* at his opponent's ships by calling out an ordered pair. Score is kept according to the number of *hits*. The purpose of the second graph is to record his own shots. There are also several versions of *tic-tac-toe*. Two teams play this game and the winner is the first team to get four points in a line. Team X has won the game shown in the figure. This game can be extended to three dimensions using plexiglas or other clear plastic and coloured counters. The plexiglas or plastic is scored to make 16 squares at each level. 3-D tic-tac-toe is won when a player succeeds in placing four counters in a straight line. horizontally. vertically or diagonally.

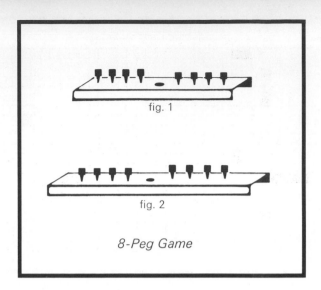

fig. 1

fig. 2

8-Peg Game

There are also a number of recreational puzzles and games where mathematical strategies are required for their solutions; for example, *Tower of Hanoi.* A game which requires a similar strategy is one in which 8 pegs or beads of two colours are arranged as in fig. 1. The object is to reverse the arrangement, as in fig. 2.

The following rules have to be observed: only one bead or peg may be moved at a time; a bead may move one hole or over one other bead only to a vacant space; beads of the same colour must always move in the same direction. The base may be of wood or plastic or even plasticene and must have nine holes.

School supply catalogues presently list many games. *Mancala* is a fascinating game over 3000 years old. *Dr. Nim* and *Think a Dot* are based on the binary number system and offer an interesting challenge. *Tuf,* based on number sentences, provokes keen interest in basic mathematical ideas.

There are many books which describe other useful games. With some encouragement, your students can devise or adapt games to reinforce many of the basic skills of mathematics. Very often, when games have been introduced into the classroom, they have been reserved for the best students as a form of reward for work well done. This is a mistake. If games do sharpen and develop useful skills, then it is the weaker student who stands to benefit most. The sensible and timely use of games can be a potent influence on changing children's attitudes toward mathematics.

Chapter 4

The Role of the Teacher

4-1 In the Classroom 55

4-2 In the School 56

4-3 In the Community 57

4-4 In Professional Preparation 59

4-5 In Workshop Planning and Participation 61

Chapter 4

The Role of the Teacher

"One-who-makes-it-possible-for-others-to-learn"

When the classroom teacher is faced with the problem of planning an active learning program designed to meet the needs of children of varying abilities, it is very different from giving the youngsters a program that is already in existence (Grade 1, Grade 2, etc.). It requires much more than the slight and reluctant modification of the program used the previous year. It requires a much greater knowledge of the background, skills and abilities of individual pupils. It requires a far broader selection of resource materials and books. In short, it requires a truly professional perform-ance that involves diagnosis, prescription, advice and encouragement, all on an individual basis.

4-1. In the Classroom

As noted above, the responsibilities of a teacher using an active learning approach are very different from those of one using a traditional approach. So much so, that many teachers question whether or not they should attempt this approach. The deciding factor is the teacher. The particular method selected must be the teacher's personal choice. Each one must be free to adapt the basic principles to suit his own personality and capabilities and those of his pupils. Identical patterns of classroom organization for all teachers are just as ridiculous as uniform standards of achievement for all children.

The essence of active learning is variety: variety in approach, in the interaction of children, and in the experiences provided for individual children. This variety in the environment is sometimes provided by the children themselves, but more often by the teacher. There is a place for all methods of learning. Some effective methods are initial class discussion of a new topic following an introduction by the teacher, investigation of problems by small groups of children, and the use of reference books, resource materials and audio-visual aids of all kinds.

It is a simple matter to identify the teacher's role when the class is working as a unit. The part the teacher plays when small groups of students are involved in active learning is more demanding, subtler, and far more rewarding. While apparatus and materials of all kinds are vital to this approach, the most influential of all aids to learning is the teacher.

Each individual student has his own particular needs. These needs depend on prior experience as well as on the stage of emotional and intellectual development reached. Once the planning is done and the groups are at work, you should move from group to group and sometimes from individual to individual, listening to the discussion. You should join in, where

The role of a teacher is different

necessary, to introduce a new word or to ask a question which will help a group to solve a problem. Tossing a child's question back at him is sometimes an effective way of encouraging him to think it out for himself. The teacher needs to know when to ask a question, when to be a silent observer and when to withdraw altogether. Children will then develop a sense of responsibility for their own intellectual growth. The teacher is not there to teach, but to encourage learning. His new role is not authoritative, but inspirational. It is as important to protect the students from too much help during the free experimentation stage as it is to ask a question to prevent a group from becoming frustrated. The pupils will need help and encouragement when they are communicating their own ideas. They will want to *practice* the new terms until these terms become familiar and are assimilated into their working vocabulary.

Later on, the teacher has another important function to fulfil — a function which is difficult to perform until he has had experience with active learning. As he goes from group to group he will identify uncertainties and weaknesses in arithmetical calculations which reveal lack of understanding. His function is to plan new work and subsequent practice to remedy these difficulties. The pupils will then gain confidence in their own ability to think for themselves.

Other objectives in planning that should concern the teacher include concept formation, ability to perform written calculations efficiently, ability to reason, creative thinking, and building adequate background knowledge. Planning the program is very important. So too are evaluating students' work and recording progress of individuals. This aspect of the work will be considered in more detail in Chapter 10.

4-2. In the School

If you are the first to introduce an active learning approach in your school, you will want to interest your colleagues in what you are doing. There are two principle ways in which this has been done:

Displays of children's work in the classroom and on the walls outside allow other children as well as teachers to see some of the interesting results.

If fire regulations allow, a large-size corrugated cardboard roll makes an excellent display surface for children's materials. Loosely snaked along a hall or around a room, supported at intervals, this material can be quickly put up or taken down, and reused many times.

Interest is often stimulated by informal and sometimes formal discussions with other teachers about the work in the classroom.

Three examples illustrating how specific schools introduced the active learning approach follow:

A display of children's work

1/ *Each of three teachers who had attended a mathematics workshop was given a teacher to sponsor. The principal took charge of each of the three classrooms in turn, so that the teachers were free to work with the colleagues they were sponsoring. In this way, the teachers gained enough confidence to make a start themselves. The principal later decided that the three teachers should run workshop sessions for the entire staff once every two weeks after school. This widened the range of grade levels included and provided additional resources for all those involved.*

2/ *A large school was represented at a workshop by a first year teacher. After she had made a start in her own classroom over a period of five weeks, she organized a workshop session for the teachers and the principal of her school. Interest was so intense that the first session lasted from 4:00 p.m. to 9:30 p.m. This was followed by additional sessions at regular intervals.*

3/ *In a few schools, a room was set aside as a mathematics room and a teacher was put in charge of developing the mathematics of the school. In the more successful programs the special teacher worked with each classroom teacher to introduce the material jointly. In this way, the teachers were able to pursue the development with their own classes. They had the additional advantage of having a teacher to whom they could turn for advice and help when they needed it.*

The role of the innovator is often a lonely one. It is possible that some colleagues will view new methods as a threat to their own security. They may be critical and unco-operative. It will require courage, patience and considerable diplomacy to carry out a program which shows the merits of an active approach to learning. As you gain confidence in your work in your own classroom, your enthusiasm may kindle interest on the part of fellow staff members. Of course, teachers who work as a team will have opportunities for an interchange of ideas and for the comparison of children's work at different stages. This mutual reinforcement lightens the load considerably.

Reference has already been made to some of the special problems of secondary schools. The role of the mathematics teacher will almost always be that of a member of a team. The habit of departmental meetings is probably firmly established so that discussion and interchange of ideas will be customary. With the continuing shift of responsibility for specific course content from extra-mural sources to the teacher, this type of dialogue is essential to a professional performance in the classroom. Topics and concepts which lend themselves to discovery techniques can be experimented with and reported on. Initial joint efforts save time and reduce the anxieties of many teachers.

4-3. In the Community

It is most important that schools working on experimental programs should establish good communications within the community. First, it is essential to maintain contact with other schools, particularly those which send pupils to you and those to which your pupils will go. These schools need to become aware of the aims and scope of the work in progress and, if possible, to see it in operation. This can best be achieved by an exchange of visits between teachers for at least a whole day. For example, the entire mathematics department of one secondary school spent three days in the classrooms of an elementary school after it had been noticed that all the pupils coming from that school showed a very special interest in and aptitude for mathematics. Holding regular workshop sessions for teachers from various schools in a community is one way of ensuring that work in mathematics is progressive and that pupil transfer from one school to another is as smooth as possible.

Secondly, it is wise to keep parents informed about the changes being made in the school program. Parents should be treated as partners if we, as teachers, are going to co-ordinate the many influences that impinge on a child. The better the understanding the less a student is pulled this way and that between adults who do not know what differences exist in the two lives he is asked to live. The key to success is communication.

It is essential that the right story goes home! Once a child has learned to read, the first question he is asked when he arrives home from school is, "What did you do in arithmetic today?" If the answer given is, "Oh, we didn't do any arithmetic today, we were pouring water into bottles," the parents might not worry for a day or two. But if similar answers are given day after day, anxiety begins to mount. The difficulty is that children working with real materials enjoy this so much that they do not consider they are learning, and hence give the impression that it is all *play*. It is necessary, therefore, that the children should know exactly what they have achieved (in terms of mathematics) so that they can take home a coherent story.

Perhaps the best way to elicit the co-operation of parents is to run a mathematics workshop for them. One principal invited the parents for an evening session. Some pupils were asked to prepare the classrooms and to assist during this session. Each parent was invited to go to his child's classrooms and to try the problems prepared for him. Seeing the consternation on the faces of many of the parents, the principal added: "Don't be worried. If you get into any difficulty, you will find some pupils in each classroom who can assist you." The principal had chosen the pupils carefully, knowing that they would answer a parent's question with another question, and not give away the answer. After an hour the parents were enjoying themselves so much that they were reluctant to leave their problems for discussion. Some of the parents had been unable to do the problems and were

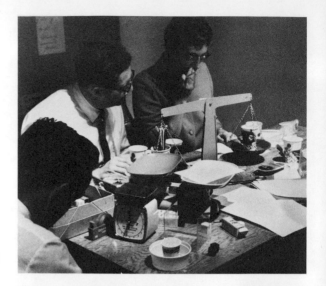

Teachers of different levels studying new methods

A display of childrens' work for parents

surprised that the pupils could tackle them. All were prepared to listen to the school's aims in the new work and to accept the fact that skill in computation was not the sole criterion on which progress should be measured. "If our children can do these difficult problems, some of which we could not do, there must be something worthwhile going on," one parent said. As a result of these workshops and of parents' interest in the day-to-day work of the school, many became involved in helping their children design and make simple pieces of apparatus (e.g., balance scales).

4-4. In Professional Preparation

Pre-Service

The only way for teachers to understand the potential of learning through discovery is to experience this at first hand themselves. It is essential that students at teachers' colleges have enough workshop sessions to become thoroughly conversant with the aims and ideals of active learning. Unless most of the student's learning comes through his own efforts, he will not leave college convinced of the value of this approach. Many college professors or lecturers are now organizing their courses to allow a substantial amount of time to be given to workshop sessions. This is especially important at the beginning of the course, not only to establish good habits of learning, but also to act as *shock* treatment to jar students out of the traditional patterns of their own schooling. Students usually identify their own deficiencies during workshop sessions and work hard to remedy these.

There is another important aspect of professional training – practice teaching. This needs to be planned with great care if students are to leave college confident enough to experiment with the first class they teach. The first essential is for the student teacher to convince himself that children can learn (mathematics, for example) through their own discoveries. For this purpose the student teacher needs to try a carefully planned piece of work on a small group of three or four children. He needs to watch the children's reactions and to ask questions to help them, but not to give the answers. In other words, he must convince himself that children do learn through experience and discovery and that it is not necessary to tell them the answers.

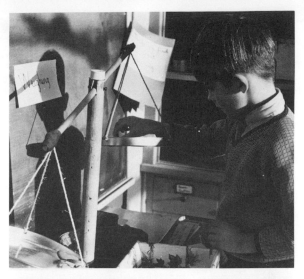

Homemade balance scale

College courses in active learning

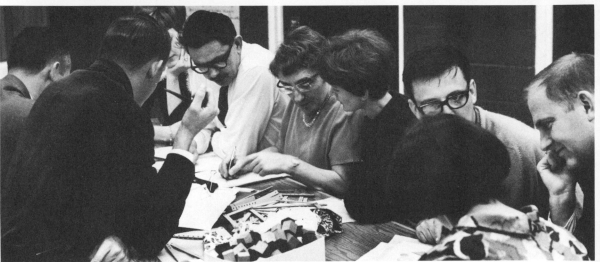

An active learning workshop

The size of the group can be increased on subsequent occasions until the student teacher is responsible for two, three or four groups at a time. In this way, although firsthand investigation makes great demands, he will gradually become accustomed to the problems which arise. Indeed, if student teachers are not given the opportunity to experiment with group work and discovery learning while in college, there is little chance that they will be confident enough to do so when they launch out on their own. If teachers at the start of their career are not prepared to organize their classrooms in this way, then the problem of in-service education will always be a formidable one.

In-Service

The great difference between instructional learning and discovery learning is not always made clear.[†] Since one is the reverse of the other, the change from one to the other may take a long time. It will probably take effect at certain grade levels and in a few classrooms as a first step. It is most important that teachers should not be coerced or overpersuaded to make changes in their classrooms before they are convinced of the need and are sufficiently confident of their own resourcefulness. If they begin with a small group of children they should not be pressed to extend the work until they feel able to do so. Above all, teachers need to be given encouragement and reassurance at every stage in their experimentation.

Workshop sessions are the most efficient means of giving teachers the help and confidence they require if they are to effect major changes in their classrooms. Workshop sessions serve several purposes:

1/ *They provide firsthand experience of learning by discovery using real materials from the environment.*

2/ *They give opportunities for the development and preparation of specific topics to cover a wide age range.*

3/ *They give opportunities for discussion and comparison of children's work. By this means it should be possible, over a long period, to build frameworks or curriculum guides.*

4/ *They extend the teacher's own mathematical background, using discovery techniques.*

4-5. In Workshop Planning and Participation

It is very important in planning a workshop that teachers from various grades should be represented, not only at each workshop, but within each working group. It is also necessary that grouping be flexible, since there may be occasions when secondary, elementary and kindergarten teachers will want to be in the same group.

The optimum size for a working group has been found to be eight. Each working group will require a tutor or helper. The total number in any workshop should be a multiple of 8. The actual number will depend on the type of workshop planned and the size of the school district.

When choosing participants it is better to have at least two teachers from a few schools than to have one from every school. It is also advisable to include the most capable and enthusiastic teachers at the first workshop because it is most important to build up a reserve of teachers able to take responsibility as tutors for future in-service training.

Various types of workshops have been tried with success. All have necessitated at least part-time release from classroom responsibilities. The minimum amount of workshop time required to give teachers confidence and substantial background is about 42 hours. During part of this time at least, the sessions should be at weekly intervals (e.g., one afternoon a week for 6, 8 or 10 weeks) so that contact can be maintained during the critical period when teachers are experimenting with their own classes. During these regular sessions it is better if numbers are kept small, not more than 24, to encourage discussion among even the more hesitant teachers.

The first workshops can be fairly large if desired, but 80 should be regarded as the maximum and smaller numbers are far more manageable. During the period of regular sessions, 40 should be the maximum. A large room is required with tables large enough for groups of eight to work comfortably. In addition, the room needs to have ample table space for materials to be set out and clearly labelled. One large display board will be required for each group.

†Chapter 1 of this text, particularly section 1-1, discusses this question.

Workshop Schedules

Finding a convenient schedule for a workshop program is one of the most difficult tasks in the planning phase. Obviously, each schedule must be adapted for a particular situation. The following suggestions may help you to develop a workshop schedule to meet the requirements in your school.

1/ *An initial 3 full days, a 6-week interval, followed by a second 3-day session. During the 6 weeks teachers will undertake to carry out a planned piece of work in their own classes. They may also choose to meet once or twice during the interval to compare results and exchange ideas. Many teachers will require further sessions in subsequent terms — perhaps 6 afternoons or evenings at weekly intervals.*

2/ *An initial 3 days followed by eight half-day sessions at weekly intervals. Because it is often difficult to release teachers during school hours, such sessions are sometimes planned for one afternoon during one week and one evening the following week.*

3/ *Eight half-day sessions at weekly intervals followed by a six-week interval during which the teachers try out a planned piece of work in the classroom. In the subsequent term another 8 sessions at weekly intervals will be required.*

4/ *Sixteen sessions over an eight-week period. An afternoon and an evening session are allocated each week for the eight-week period.*

5/ *Summer sessions of two or more weeks. Each day consists of two 3-hour periods with coffee breaks and lunch as desired. Some universities are conducting workshops such as this as part of their regular summer program.*

In summary we must remember that the classroom teacher is the agent of change. In the past and in many schools today, he *is* the curriculum and the classroom is but a reflection of his personality and attitude towards learning. In order to implement active learning, the role of the teacher must be one of true professionalism, inspiration, skill, dedication and responsibility.

Chapter 5

The Role of the Principal

5-1 In the School   65

5-2 In Implementing an Innovative Program 66

5-3 In Organization   68

5-4 In Record Keeping   70

5-5 In Relation to Children   70

5-6 In the School System   72

5-7 In the Community   73

Another one-who-makes-it-possible-for-others-to-learn!

The principal of a school is in a strategic position when innovations in the educational program are being considered. While the amount of freedom and personal responsibility for the operation of his school varies widely from one school district to another, it is the principal who sets the tone for the learning that takes place in his school. It does not really matter whether the policies of the local school system require that he be the principal-teacher or more of an administrator; his position and the attitudes he brings to it set the stage for the performance of both teachers and students in the educational process.

It is not the purpose of this chapter to suggest qualifications for the principal, either academic or personal, or to recommend policy changes that would affect the operation of the school. The wide range of physical facilities, the great variations in professional competence of teachers, the needs of students, and the tradition and desires of different communities make it impossible to set down detailed plans and procedures for implementing a program that is child-centered rather than subject-centered. We understand and appreciate the heavy pressures that bear upon the principal from pupils, teachers, parents and a hierarchy of officials, to maintain a stable, smooth-running, educational institution. Change is rarely accomplished smoothly. It requires

considerable courage, conviction and determination to instigate and support innovations that will *rock the boat* as far as the present organizational patterns are concerned. The ideas and suggestions presented here have been drawn from the experience of many principals who have committed themselves to the role of curriculum leaders in their schools. These ideas and suggestions are offered in the hope that they will increase the courage, intensify the conviction, and double the determination of those principals who are concerned with improving the quality and effectiveness of their school program.

5-1. In the School

Over a period of years, the school principal has been described as the key figure in determining the atmosphere for learning that exists in his school. The concept of the principal as the primary person responsible for all that goes on within the confines of his building in terms of instruction has gained widespread acceptance in the mind of the public. This belief has been carefully nurtured and strengthened by the general practice of having the principal responsible for the organization of classes, promotion or non-promotion of students, discipline, attendance reports and so on. In short, it is the principal who has the most frequent contact with parents and the public. Through

65

letters, notices and reports or by means of interviews and speeches he has the opportunity to establish himself as the authority responsible for the role the school plays in the growth of children. The opportunity has not been wasted. But the image of the principal as the leader in method and curriculum is largely a myth. Those who are, or have been principals know that the policies of local authorities, the quality of the staff, the allocation of funds, the facilities available, the attitudes of the parents, and many other factors influence the quality of education in a school to a much greater degree. The typical school principal is much more a manager than an educational leader. In many cases, he is little more than a highly paid clerk since school boards generally fail to provide adequate secretarial assistance to handle the bulk of administrative detail. Because of the attitude of the hierarchy in education, many principals retreat to the relative security of their office, abandoning their role in the instructional process and contenting themselves with a kind of executive dexterity.

How can a conscientious principal who senses the discrepancy between what he is able to do and his public image as an educational leader, really set the tone for his school? From the experience of many principals the answer appears to lie in the sharing or delegating of responsibility. The key to this problem is the mutual respect and trust which exists between the principal and his colleagues. It is the same relationship that should exist between the teacher and his pupils before a really desirable climate for learning can be established. Teachers cannot be expected to encourage children to display initiative and discover things for themselves if they themselves are not allowed freedom to use their own initiative and plan programs that truly meet the needs of the children in their classes. In this respect the principal must have confidence in individual teachers and be thoroughly convinced of the merit of such a program. Both circumstances are prerequisites for the establishment of a flexible, child-centered program.

The principal who wishes to function as the curriculum leader of his school should be prepared to act as a consultant, advisor and co-ordinator. The great majority of his time will be spent with children and teachers, helping them to use their energies and talents in the most effective way possible. He will marshal all the resources that will complement and amplify the learning experiences of the pupils. He will act as the leader of a team, a team composed of all the personnel of the school, sharing such activities as school policy-making, curriculum revision, in-service professional activities, and interpreting the school to the community. The kind of leadership that provides for a co-operative approach to choices and decisions is likely to ensure a better attitude and greater understanding on the part of teachers as well as to promote their self-improvement and growth. The enrichment of the school environment for teachers will lead to a more vital, stimulating and satisfying program for children.

5-2. In Implementing an Innovative Program

The first step towards the introduction of an innovative program is for the principal to be convinced that such a program is in the best interests of the children in the school. This conviction, and the knowledge and understanding necessary to support it, can only be acquired through firsthand experience with the process. In-service education of principals is essential. Some experimental programs require the attendance of principals at workshops as well as teachers from participating schools. Our experience in school systems suggests that the degree of success in developing and implementing an active child-centered program is directly proportional to the number of principals who participate in the in-service program. When principals have had the opportunity to explore and discover in the same way as children, they appreciate the benefits of learning in this way and are far more ready to assist and encourage teachers. In fact, the attitude and understanding of the principal is significantly more influential in the continuing success of the program than materials, equipment, facilities; indeed, everything but the conviction of the teacher himself.

Principals involved in active learning

Administrator encouraging new methods in
the classroom

Teachers look for support from the principal in several ways. First, they need and deserve his continuing help and encouragement in sustaining their own self-confidence. The role of an innovating teacher is often lonely and frustrating. This, coupled with the criticism of colleagues who view change as a threat to their own security, is enough to discourage all but the strongest teachers. The public approval and active assistance of the principal is usually enough to strengthen their conviction and to encourage other teachers to make a start in their own classrooms.

Secondly, they need his help in obtaining the necessary equipment and materials. This is one of the areas where team planning can make the best use of that very limited resource in schools — money. Too often the budget is dispersed without agreement on priorities. The consequent disappointment and frustration on the part of teachers could be avoided if they understood and were prepared for the restrictions that lack of funds impose. When emergencies do arise and teachers know they can count on the support of the principal in reaching some sort of satisfactory compromise, they are less inclined to use financial excuses for not trying something new in their classrooms.

Thirdly, teachers need time — time for discussion with colleagues, time for planning and preparation, time to visit other classes, time for evaluation and reflection. Some of this time should be made available during school hours. Teachers are beginning to resent the rapidly accelerating demands on their out-of-school time. No business or industrial concern in the country expects its professional staff to keep abreast of developments in their particular field during their own time. Educational authorities are just beginning to realize the need for release time for the professional growth of their teachers. In the meantime, the principal can exhibit his personal interest in the program by freeing teachers from their classroom duties for varying periods. There are several ways of doing this:

1/ *Arranging for supply teachers or consultants to take the class for all or a part of the day.*
2/ *Working with the children himself either in the classroom or in the auditorium.*
3/ *Planning special programs that will allow the grouping of several classes in a large area.*

4/ *Relieving teachers of playground or lunch-room supervision at recess or during the noon hour.*
5/ *Undertaking some pioneering in the use of adult assistants — parents interested in the school or young adults contemplating careers in education.*

The strategies or techniques the principal uses to provide time for his teachers are relatively unimportant. What is significant is that by his actions he is demonstrating his wholehearted support for the innovation; this is far more reassuring to experimenting teachers than are any compliments. Furthermore, by his personal commitment, the principal is developing an ideal relationship with his staff — one of mutual trust and respect.

5-3. In Organization

There are many other practices in today's schools which tend to restrict innovation and handicap adventurous teachers. These can be loosely grouped into one category and labelled organizational or administrative devices. Here the leadership of the principal is essential.

Let us consider timetables first. One of the time-honoured traditions of elementary schools is the practice of requiring teachers to submit detailed timetables that account for every single minute of the school day. (In many secondary schools timetables are prepared for the teacher.) These are approved by the principal if they show a reasonable allocation of time for each discipline and if consideration has been given to the varying attention spans of children of different ages. Who is in a better position to decide the best use of the time a child is in school than the classroom teacher? Is this practice symptomatic of the degree of trust and respect we have for the professional judgment of others? A disgruntled superintendent of schools in a small city put it this way: "If I wanted to organize a school that would deliberately make children dull, I would arrange it so that the moment they were interested in doing something I would ring a bell, and make them stop, and begin something else." Timetables are needed when it is necessary to share special facilities such as gymnasiums, music rooms or resource centres. Otherwise, it does seem unreasonable to break up the day into comparatively short sessions when the whole emphasis should be on continuity. When children are thoroughly absorbed in investigation or experiment it would be quite wrong to expect them to break off and then continue at some future time with the same enthusiasm. Planning is needed and some scheduling is necessary but it should be done over longer periods, possibly between two weeks and a month, and involve larger blocks of time.

Timetables should guide and not dominate the learning experiences that take place in the classroom. They are most effective when they are prepared jointly by the teacher and students with the principal acting as a consultant. They should be flexible enough to allow for the foreseeable events as well as some of the unforeseeable, and should be susceptible to frequent revision.

Within the policies of the local authority for education, the principal should examine the purpose, timing and usefulness of term and final examinations. All too often the examination is used as an instrument to put pressure on children to generate more intense effort. "You will not pass the exam" or "just wait till your parents see your mark" are threats common in many classrooms. Fear of failure is neither desirable nor effective as a motivational force for young children. Furthermore, when the examination is administered to whole classes it requires every student to follow the same path to learning and to travel at the same speed. Both of these conditions are alien to the spirit and objectives of a child-centered program that allows for individual differences in ability and provides a wide variety of experiences that have meaning for children.

External examinations designed by someone outside the school and administered at a set time each year are particularly damaging. These are often used to determine promotion or failure. When used in this way, they constitute a threat to the educational progress of each child and, indirectly, to the reputation of the teacher and the standards of the school. Passing-the-exam-hysteria dominates the planning, the teaching and the learning for the whole year. This external pressure to achieve a common standard frequently places children in a position where they resort to any means to reduce the chances of failing. The subsequent last-minute cramming or even cheating has undersirable long-term effects.

Assessment of students by large scale, multiple-choice, computer-scored achievement tests should also be examined carefully. Such tests are in reality crude instruments which cannot measure the depth, subtlety or originality of the child's thinking. When children are encouraged to think for themselves, to form opinions about what they learn, and to support ideas in one field of study by examining their relationship to ideas in other fields, rigid multiple-choice tests could be exceedingly frustrating to them. The extreme care with which such tests should be used is illustrated in the following account.

A large city school system used nationally standardized achievement tests in several subjects to select children for enrichment or advanced study classes. A principal who had been experimenting with a program that stressed individual growth and that depended on the provision of a great variety of resource materials, duly administered the tests at the appropriate times to several classes of very able seven-year-olds. He was astonished to find that the children fared very badly – in the 40th percentile range – according to their grade norms. Unable to believe the results, he administered the test for the next higher grade to the same students. The results were significantly better – in the 60th percentile. He then chose a test used for children two grades higher and the results moved upward toward the 90th percentile. The principal deduced that the very tests used to identify gifted students discriminated against them! Discussion with the children revealed that they could not believe that the correct response could be so simple and obvious. They were reading far more difficulty into the questions than that which existed. Needless to say, the selection procedures in this system were soon changed.

There are distinct advantages in teacher-designed tests. They can be tailored to suit the objectives determined by the teacher for a particular group of students. The tests can be administered at any time to any group which is ready to be examined. Children are much more receptive to a diagnostic type evaluation of their understanding of a single concept or skill than to the random sampling of the learning that has taken place over a term or a year. The test should become an integral part of the learning process, welcomed by the pupils as an opportunity to identify their difficulties, and by the teacher, as an instrument to measure the effectiveness of his teaching.

The principal can encourage teachers to develop better instruments for assessing progress by giving them the responsibility for this and demonstrating his confidence in their judgment. There is no substitute for the mediating influence of the classroom teacher on any instrument that purports to measure learning. In any evaluation procedure due consideration should be given to the teacher's own assessment of individual children.

5-4. In Record Keeping

Where there is a change in the techniques of assessing children's learning, record keeping and reporting procedures should be revised. Such revision should be a co-operative venture between the principal and his staff with the principal acting more or less as the control agent. He must accommodate the changes to such policy as is determined by the local board of education or secure permission to experiment within certain boundaries. Since the techniques of evaluation and suggestions for recording pupil progress will be presented in Chapter 10, it is not appropriate to dwell at any length on this topic here. The significant aspect at this moment is the role of the principal in facilitating such change. It is the responsibility of the principal, in most systems, to arrange the children in classes, assign these to teachers, and maintain adequate records as evidence for parents and others on the progress of individual children. He must be sure that the information he has is up-to-date and reliable. The principal should seek some happy balance between the time-consuming, detailed, objective type reports and the child's own account of his progress supplemented by samples of his work. Here is an opportunity to share an administrative function, to show interest in and respect for the opinions of others.

The principal's role in the classroom

5-5. In Relation to Children

So far, the suggestions offered concerning the role of the principal in developing a child-centered program have been focussed on his function as a leader. Except by implication, no mention has been made of his relationship to the children in his school. Earlier, it was suggested that the great majority of the principal's time should be spent with teachers and children. It is this contact with children that will create an image of the principal in the minds of the children. Whether the image is that of a friendly, sympathetic and understanding adult who inspires trust and respect or of a distant, preoccupied, authoritarian figure who legislates, investigates, arbitrates and punishes, depends largely on whether the contact is made on the student's *home ground* – the classroom, or on the principal's *home ground* – the office. Naturally, there will be interactions in both situations and the outcome will be determined in large measure by the sensitivity and genuine affection the principal has for children. Several principals feel that it is essential to have the first contact in the classroom because many of the official contacts in the office have to do with discipline or investigations into problems that cause a good deal of anxiety in the mind of the child. The following poem by John W. Sullivan paints a clear and compassionate picture.

Justice

So he stands before you
Having been brought fresh from his crimes
To be dealt with by
The 'Authority.'
You say,
'Well, what happened to you?'
Even though you know what happened
Because you have heard it from a teacher
Whom he called a 'dirty bastard'
And you have heard it from a little girl
Who has a bleeding cheek and lacerated lip
As evidence of her encounter with reality.
So he, and the teacher, and the little girl,
All want Justice.
You look at the hanging head, shrugged shoulders,
Hands caked with yesterday's mud,
Open-toed running shoes,
And you wonder 'why.'
You know that there is not an answer,
But you still wonder.
All the bright, trite phrases of your training
Knock on your mind —
Poverty syndrome, cultural deviation, aggression,
    frustration —
They knock on your mind,
But somehow they don't seem pertinent.
O, they fit all right.
But each time your mind lets them in
It answers a vernacular
'So what!'
And the teacher's voice has said,
'What are you going to do about it?'
And the little girl's eyes have said,
'What are you going to do about it?'
And you are left alone with him
To find the answers.
To find justice.
But do we know where justice is?
Whose justice?
Society's justice?
Little boy's justice?
Little girl's justice?
Teacher's justice?
Is there one justice — a rule, a guide,
A star to follow?
You don't remember it from a university text,
Or from a Superintendent's letter,
Or from the Minister's Report.
Perhaps Glick, or Blatz, or Smith has the answer.

Or Cuscizinski or Mrs. Littlestope.
You wonder should people write books
With a kid in front of them.
Maybe we'd get more meat and less potatoes
    if they did.
Mashed potatoes, creamed and buttered,
But nothing about justice. Not this justice anyway.
What did The Russian say about crime and
    punishment?
You think he must have said something in all
    those pages
But it eludes your grasp.
So he stands before you waiting,
Without anger
Which has been spent.
Without fear,
Except for an inner fear that has become a way
    of life,
And is not felt separately in him.
Perhaps just resignation.
Like the resignation of a trapped field mouse.
So you must take action. Action.
The strap?
As though the way to a boy's heart is through
    his hands.
Suspension?
As though greater exposure to those who made
    him crooked
Would make him straight.
Talk? Compassion? Forgiveness? Your wisdom wilts.
What about Justice?

The role of the principal in the school is
remarkably similar to that of the teacher in the
classroom. To a young child they are both *big*
people. The attitude and approach of one should
be reinforced by the attitude and approach of the
other. Otherwise, tensions and anxieties
are built up as the child tries to attune himself
first to one, then the other. The principal-child
relationship should be one of mutual trust
and respect. The school should be a place where
friends can learn together. The satisfaction that
comes from seeing boys and girls developing
alert and versatile minds, purposeful minds that
parents want, comprehending and constructive
minds that society requires, is a measure of the
principal's success.

Administrator visiting an active learning school

5-6. In the School System

It is a wise principal who works closely with his fellow principals and the senior officials of the school system. Just as teachers enlist the support and assistance of their colleagues within a school, principals should utilize the variety of experiences and training of their associates by inviting their comments on any innovative program. In most cases, it is essential that the local senior administrative official be aware of the experiment and give his approval.

The sympathy and understanding of fellow principals can be of tremendous help. Should it be necessary to effect some modification or even a complete change in the policy of the local administration so that the experimental program may flourish and expand, those in responsible positions must be prepared to support the reform. While it is unlikely that there will be unanimous agreement among any group of educators, a continuing effort to keep the others informed will pay dividends in the long run, not only in support of new ideas but in the scope and richness of the suggestions that may help in avoiding some of the pitfalls that plague innovation and experiment.

The principals of elementary, intermediate and secondary schools should be aware of the objectives and the techniques that characterize a child-centered program. It is important that the transfer of pupils from one school to another should be as smooth as possible. This aspect of new programs is of particular concern to parents. Very often the only frame of reference parents have is their own experience in school, or perhaps that of an older son or daughter. They need to be assured that participation in an experimental program will in no way handicap their children for later work. One of the most effective ways to achieve this assurance is for parents to witness the active co-operation of the principals concerned.

A principal might attempt to influence his associates in many possible ways. These will depend largely on his own personality, his record as a leader in curriculum reform, and his past experience with the individuals with whom he works. Many principals, experienced and inexperienced, have found the techniques they use with teachers equally effective with principals.

The first step is to get them interested. This is usually accomplished by inviting them to visit classrooms to observe the students in action. Displays of children's work, statements by participating teachers and the obvious belief of the principal that such a method is practical and appropriate for the boys and girls in his school are the most convincing arguments of all.

The second step is to get principals to understand the aims and objectives of the program. The best method is to give them an opportunity to explore and discover in the same way as the children. The workshop program described in Chapter 6 has been most effective when used for this purpose. Not only does it give principals insight into the learning process but it helps them to appreciate the excitement and enthusiasm children display when they are set free to think for themselves.

The time is long past when principals (and teachers) jealously guarded their own successful techniques and used them for their own professional advancement. When opportunities are provided for principals to share their professional experiences with the entire school, the ultimate advantage accrues to the children. While the participating principals grow both in breadth of vision and in experience, the children benefit from the accumulated wisdom of their educational leaders and the prospect of continuity in their school environment.

5-7. In the Community

The role of the principal in the school system and the role of the principal in the community are very similar. For the purposes of this chapter, the difference is simply the relationship between professional educators as distinct from that between the educator and the general public. In practice, the leadership role of the principal spreads across the two dimensions without any significant discrimination.

The principal of a school has a vital responsibility for maintaining links with the community his school serves. A school must be sensitive to the nature, needs and desires of the community; to know what these are the principal must enter into community life. His participation can take many forms, most of them informal and individual.

Some dialogue should be established if there is to be harmony between two of the most significant influences on a child's life — the home and the school. The role of the principal in this respect is somewhat different from that of the classroom teacher since he, by the nature of his position, must accept the responsibility for the total program of the school. His contact with parents, while perhaps more infrequent and less personal, is regarded as *official*.

The leadership of the principal should be directed largely toward improved communication between the home and the school. The experiences of many principals would indicate that communication is the key to developing parents' confidence in the professional competence of the staff and consequently their support for innovation. Once parents are convinced that proposed changes are in the best interests of their children, they will support them wholeheartedly. Frequently, this endorsement by the community is of great help in acquiring better facilities and equipment for a program.

The greatest *salesmen* for any school are the children themselves. If they are happy, interested and enjoying some measure of success each day, they will be eager to get to school in the morning and will continue their experiments and investigations on their own time at home. This total involvement with learning is one of the exciting by-products of a child-centered program. It provides the hope for overcoming the age-old problem of getting the parents to participate in the life of the school.

One of the most effective, yet seldom used ways of interpreting the school program to parents is to invite them to school to observe children in action. Too often this approach is reserved for special occasions such as Education Week, Parents' Day, Christmas, or a program of music or physical education. While final arrangements are the responsibility of the classroom teacher, the principal can facilitate such public relations by co-ordinating the program, arranging for assistance, and demonstrating his own enthusiasm by participating in it. Parents gain valuable insight and are more inclined to support the school program when they observe their child in his other life at school. Initially, the teacher or principal should be ready to explain what is happening and why. This

73

Parents discussing pupil's work

is a matter of courtesy, but it is more than that:
it suggests the readiness of the educator to have
the parents comment on the program; it demonstrates respect for their opinions. Respect is just as
critical in parent-teacher relations as it is in pupil-
teacher or principal-teacher situations.

As a result of this face-to-face contact, principals
will discover many parents with special skills and
abilities. This is a community resource that is
usually ignored and yet it has great potential, both
for the school program and good public relations.
It is the principal's responsibility to take the
initiative in organizing this resource to the best
advantage.

There are many other ways of gaining community acceptance and support. One of the areas
that causes the greatest difficulty and most mis-
understanding is in the communication of
children's progress. Measurement and reporting
procedures will be dealt with more thoroughly in
Chapter 10. For the moment, it is enough to identify
this aspect of the program as the responsibility of
the principal.

Underlying and permeating all aspects of the
role of the principal is the respect he shows for
others. If this is exhibited in his relations with
pupils, parents, teachers and other officials in the
school system, all else will fall into place. Regard
for the feelings of others, tact, sympathy and
friendliness will be his trademark. Instead of "my"
school it will be "our" school — for the children,
the parents, the staff, and indeed, for the whole
community.

Chapter 6

A Typical Workshop Program

6-1   General Comments   77

6-2   Working Sessions 1 and 2   80

6-3   Working Sessions 3 and 4   81

6-4   Working Sessions 5 and 6   84

6-5   Working Session 7   84

6-6   Working Sessions 8, 9 and 10   87

6-7   Working Sessions 11 and 12   87

6-8   The 6-Week Interval   87

6-9   Working Sessions 13 and 14   87

6-10   Working Sessions 15 and 16   94

6-11   Working Sessions 17 and 18   94

6-12   Working Session 19   99

6-13   Working Session 20 and part of 21   101

6-14   Working Sessions 21 and 22   101

6-15   Working Sessions 23 and 24   108

The program described in this chapter is the 3-day, 6-week, 3-day schedule. Such a program consists of 3 days of workshop experiences, followed by a 6-week interval in which participants undertake to carry on a planned piece of work with children, concluding with another 3 days of workshop activities. We feel this type of program has more advantages than the others (see section 4-5) and should be followed. If such a schedule is not possible, the following sessions can be adapted to other workshop schedules.

While the activities outlined in the following pages have evolved from our work with practicing teachers, the purpose and experience applies equally well to teachers-in-training. Colleges can readily develop a workshop program on a continuing basis with their students. It is important that educators break the practice of lecturing only and provide opportunities for college students to experience the challenge of learning in an active way. Several universities are presently incorporating active learning or "learning-through-doing" sessions in their pre-service programs. The college program has an even greater potential of being related to other aspects of the curriculum than an in-service program. We firmly believe that students themselves need considerable experience using active learning if they are to introduce and use this approach in their own classrooms. Since there is no one way to develop this type of program, it is essential that college students as well as experienced teachers work with a variety of materials in a

wide range of problem situations. In this manner they can develop confidence in their own ability to stimulate learning through enquiry.

It is our intention that the approach described in this chapter be used as a guide to stimulate thought and create ideas. We encourage those in charge of setting up such a program to make changes to adapt these suggestions to suit their own situations.

6-1. General Comments

We feel the workshop program can be carried out most effectively in a large room, such as a gymnatorium. The room should contain tables, each large enough for eight adults to work comfortably. In addition, there should be ample shelf or table space for materials to be set out and clearly labelled. The materials and equipment can best be arranged under the following labels: length, weight, capacity, time, round shapes, rectangular shapes, various shapes, dry goods, structural materials, materials for communication (paper, paint, paste, magic markers, etc.). A large display board is needed for each group and a wastebasket should be strategically placed.

3 Day – 6 Week – 3 Day Schedule

	9:15 – 10:45	11:00 – 12:30	2:00 – 3:30	3:45 – 5:15
Day 1	Vital Statistics		Mathematics in the Environment (Measurement)	
	1	2	3	4
Day 2	Three- and Two-Dimensional Shapes		Arithmetic – A New Look	Development of a Topic (Pupil Level)
	5	6	7	8
Day 3	Development of a Topic (Pupil Level)		Summary and Examples of Children's Work	Area Group Discussions
	9	10	11	12
		6-Week Interval		
Day 4	Patterns in Statistics		Review and Discussion of Pupils' Work of 6-Week Interval	
	13	14	15	16
Day 5	Patterns in Shapes		Patterns in Graphs	Development of a Topic (Pupil Level)
	17	18	19	20
Day 6	Development of a Topic (Pupil Level)	Patterns in Numbers and Algebra	Summary and Group Discussions	Planning For the Future
	21	22	23	24

Again we would like to emphasize that it is advantageous to form the groups for these workshops so that they contain teachers of various grade levels, both sexes, and where possible, superintendents and principals. We would also suggest that teachers from the same schools be separated so as to have a variety of situations represented at each table.

It is practical to divide each day into four working sessions as follows: 9:15 – 10:45, 11:00 – 12:30, 2:00 – 3:30, 3:45 – 5:15. Such a schedule allows time for morning and afternoon coffee breaks. If the school is in session while the workshop is going on, it is wise to avoid congestion at assembly and dismissal times for the pupils.

The table above shows the schedule described in this chapter.

Because adults have been continually subjected to learning through the traditional, directed methods, they often experience great difficulty in shifting from this method to the more flexible, active learning approach. For this reason the structure of the workshop sessions has been organized to expedite learning on an adult level. In general, the first sessions are carefully directed, the middle sessions less directed and the final sessions are devoted to extending the mathematical background of the teachers, using the active learning approach.

It is important to note, at this point, that children are more flexible than adults in accepting new approaches to learning. Usually, the younger the child, the easier it is for him to adjust to an active learning approach without a transitional period.

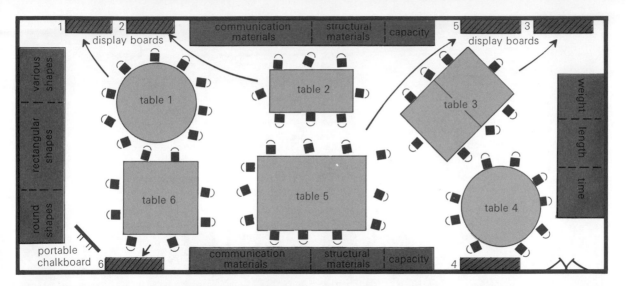

The diagram shows a typical workshop room arrangement:

- 1, 2 — display boards
- communication materials | structural materials | capacity
- 5, 3 — display boards
- various shapes
- rectangular shapes
- round shapes
- table 1
- table 2
- table 3
- weight
- length
- time
- table 6
- table 5
- table 4
- portable chalkboard
- 6
- communication materials | structural materials | capacity
- 4

*A typical room
arrangement for a workshop*

79

Workshop courses in college

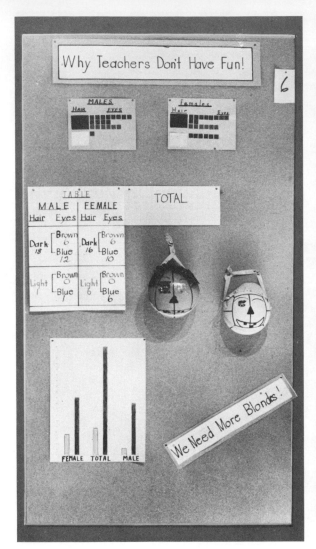

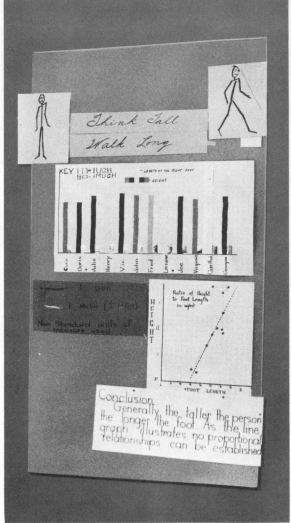

Some results of the Vital Statistics Unit

6-2. Working Sessions 1 and 2

The aims of the first sessions are to put teachers at their ease, to accustom them to working with colleagues from other grades and to become familiar with a wide range of materials. (See section 3-2.) A unit of vital statistics has been found most useful in this respect. In this session each group is asked to make some unusual and interesting comparisons about themselves. Here are some examples of the topics frequently chosen:

Comparison of cubit, or span, of height, and of length of pace
Size of family and position of the teacher within the family (first born, etc.)

Comparison of strength and of weight
Lung capacity
Pulse rate before and after exercise

The tutors (or helpers) are asked to let the groups select their own topic. To prevent overlap each group records its choice on the blackboard on a *first come, first served* basis. Each group is asked to communicate the sets of measurements and its observations in at least six different ways, including pictorial representations, graphs, tabular forms and a written comment. A great variety of materials should be available. The use of rulers or tape measures should be discouraged. We feel that emphasis should be placed on the attractiveness and creativeness of the presentation.

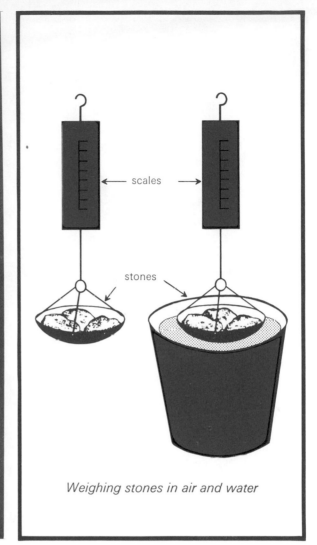

Weighing stones in air and water

This session gives the tutors an opportunity to discuss various points with the group, such as (1) the need to include zero, (2) the appropriate types of representation for the small sample available (pictorial, block or column graphs are appropriate; but a line graph is inappropriate), and (3) the introduction of other ways of presenting the results (scale drawings, pie charts or forms of mapping). Towards the end of the session each group is asked to arrange its representations on the display boards to illustrate the mathematical development. The groups then examine the other presentations and summaries are made.

6-3. Working Sessions 3 and 4

Each group selects a topic for investigation at an adult level from the following: weight, capacity, time, length, rate and ratio, proportion, perimeter and area, averages, conservation, inequalities or number patterns. (The topic the group selects will be used for the preparation of open-ended questions and development at pupil level in working sessions 8, 9 and 10.) Some of the questions used to start the investigation at adult level follow:

Weight

1/ *Which is heaviest, rice, beans or water?*
Find out in more than one way and comment on

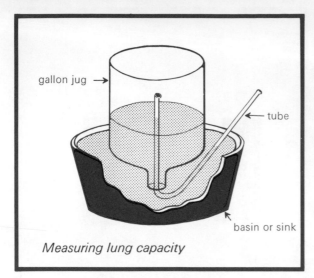

gallon jug →

→ tube

→ basin or sink

Measuring lung capacity

your results. (The weights of equal volumes of these commodities are first compared; an apparently contradictory result is obtained when rice and beans do not float when they are dropped into water. Explain why this happens. This discussion leads to the next question.) What fraction of space is taken up by air in a cup of marbles?

2/ *Find the weight of a single pin, thumb tack, pea or bean. Use two different methods and comment on the reliability of your results. (Usually an ounce or half-ounce of each is weighed, the weight is fixed, and the number of objects are counted. For the second method the number is usually fixed at 100 and the weight is found. Converting to decimals may be necessary in order to be able to compare the results. Reliability depends on the quantity weighed.)*

3/ *Do stones weigh the same, weigh more, or weigh less when suspended in water? Check to see if you were right and comment on your results. Why can you float in water? About how many times as heavy as water is your stone? Is there a relationship between the weight and volume of the stones? Would a graph help? (For this question at least 5 stones of weights between 1 and 5 lbs. are required. Some groups will want to construct their own scales for weighing.)*

Capacity

1/ *Estimate, then find your lung capacity in pints. Is there a sex difference in lung capacities? (For this investigation some rubber tubing and a large container with a cork or screw-cap are needed. The experiment is best carried out in a sink with a stopper or plug.)*

2/ *How many marbles would occupy the same space as a ball? Estimate first, then test your answer. What fraction of a cupful of marbles is air?*

3/ *Make a careful estimate of the number of small containers required to fill a large container. Check to see if you were right. (For this experiment, two containers of similar shape, but of different sizes are required, such as small and large cylindrical tins, small and large bottles or jugs. Estimates may be made by matching one against the other but not by actual measurement. The check is made by filling the two containers and comparing their capacities.)*

4/ *How many grains of rice in a one-pound coffee can?*

Time

1/ *Can you change the beat of a pendulum? In how many different ways can you do this? (Change only one variable in each experiment.) Does a simple pendulum beat regularly? Test this in two different ways and comment on your results. (A good point of suspension must be found. Uniform sizes of metal washers or plasticene can be used for the pendulum bob.)*

2/ *Estimate the speed of a toy truck (a spring-wound one is best). Find the speed using two different methods and comment on your results. (A graph may help you to avoid calculations.) What additional variables do you introduce when you run the truck down a ramp? (Investigate these, changing one variable at a time. The truck will need to run down a rail; otherwise it will run off the ramp. A similar problem can be investigated by rolling a marble or a small ball down a trough or a piece of curtain railing. In either case, several new variables have been introduced.) Is the speed now constant?*

3/ *Investigate the regularity of your pulse, the length of your pace and your walking speed. Could you use your pulse to measure time?*

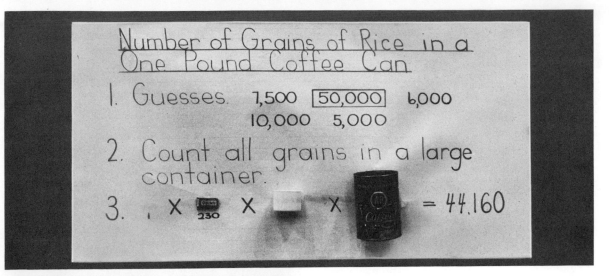

*Chart showing how one group counted
the grains of rice*

Estimating the speed of a toy truck

Length

1/ *Could you use your pace to estimate a distance? Find the length of your pace in two distinct
ways. Use your pace to estimate a distance and
see how close you are to the measured distance.*

2/ *Is there a relationship between air fares and
distance travelled? Use a string to find distances
between various cities on a globe. Apply what
you know about the circumference of the earth at
the equator to develop a ready reckoner or scale.
Use this, or any other distance you know, to
obtain the correct scale for your piece of string.
Compare your results with those given on the map
showing flight distances for aircraft.*

3/ *Peg out, by eye, a regular triangle with sides
10 yards in length on the playground or lawn.
(Do not use any lines to help you.) Take measurements which will enable you to make a map of the
triangle. How accurate were you? Repeat, pegging
out a square with sides 10 yards in length. (This
time measuring the 4 sides will be insufficient
to fix the square. Why?)*

4/ *Find the thickness of a drinking straw, a sheet of paper and a piece of string. Use two methods and comment on the reliability of your results. (Refer to question 2 on weight.)*

5/ *Find the length, width and height of the auditorium by a number of methods, with and without measuring instruments. Comment on the reliability of your results. What is the ratio of the length, width and height?*

Each group divides into twos or threes to work at a question. These questions are intended as starting points only and may be developed according to the wishes of the individuals. The results of each investigation are recorded in different ways and displayed on the bulletin boards. Time should be given for each group to examine the work done at the other tables.

Since it usually will not take all of Session 4 to complete this unit we have found it profitable to use the latter part of Session 4 to show a film like *Maths Alive*. (See section 3-5.) It is also advisable to spend some time in question-and-answer or in group discussion to clear up any concerns participants may have about the active learning approach. Such a session is often useful in keying tutors towards special points that should be emphasized or experiences that should be provided in future sessions.

6-4. Working Sessions 5 and 6

Working sessions 5 and 6 are given to an investigation of three- and two-dimensional shapes. Each group is given the same assignments but is encouraged to develop these in individual ways. It is usual to have a wide variety of presentations.

Material for each table includes:
At least 30 identical cardboard rectangular boxes
At least 30 coloured identical cubes
20 post cards or 5″ by 8″ file cards
1 *halo* (loop of construction paper ½ inch wide and 20 inches long)
A supply of 1″ squared paper, scissors, construction paper in bright colours, 1″ gummed squares (coloured).

The groups are given the following questions for investigation.

1/ Make successively larger models of the unit box or cube. What things are changing? (Volume, surface area, perimeter, weight) What remains the same? Find the patterns of the sequences you obtain. Either draw a graph or make a table and continue the patterns as far as you can. Compare lengths of successive edges, successive volumes, successive surface areas.

What do you notice about these patterns? What is the sequence of ratios of the surface area to the volume? (How many squares for each cube?)

2/ Can you change the area enclosed by your halo? If so, what is the shape of (a) the largest, (b) the smallest areas you can enclose? What is the largest rectangular shape you can make? (Make the complete sequence of rectangles having sides an integral number of units. If you cut them out of coloured paper try to arrange the rectangles so that they occupy minimum area while still preserving the sequence.)

3/ What is the reverse of this problem? If you fix the area, do you fix the perimeter? Take 2 squares. How many shapes can you make in which the squares have at least one common point? How does the perimeter change? Repeat this experiment with 3 squares, 4 squares, etc.

6-5. Working Session 7

In this session a new approach to arithmetic is considered. In particular, initial experiences which will eventually enable children to devise their own methods of computation are suggested and discussed by teachers. These experiences will involve the operations of addition, subtraction, multiplication and division, and our written number system. We suggest the notes on page 86 be distributed to the tutors before the workshop and to the teachers during session 12. In this session teachers are asked to devise simple experiences which they could give children to introduce them to the operations of addition, subtraction, multiplication and division. Materials used in this session are not necessarily appropriate for young children.

Edge	Volume	Surface Area
0	0	0
1	1	6
2	8	24
3	27	54
4	64	96
5	125	150
6	216	216
7	343	294
8	512	384

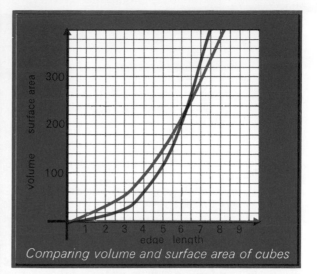

Comparing volume and surface area of cubes

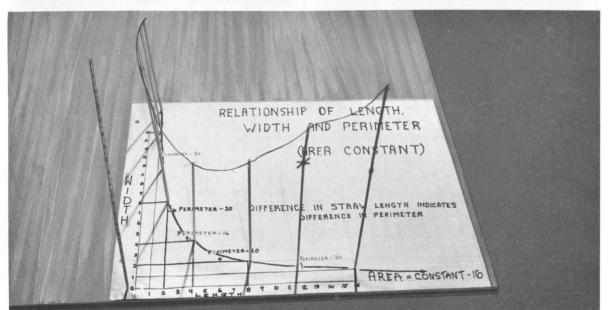

*A three-dimensional graph comparing length,
width, and perimeter*

Mathematical Structure – Length – Capacity – Money – Weight – Time

Teachers are asked to devise simple experiences which they could give children to introduce them to the operations of addition, subtraction, multiplication and division. Materials used in this session are not necessarily appropriate for young children.

Structure: A small uncounted pile of pebbles, acorns or bottle caps for each two partners.
1. Separate the pebbles into two unequal piles. Without actually counting, set out the exact number of pebbles which is the difference between these two piles. What operation did you use? (Matching, one-to-one correspondence.)
2. Using matching, arrange successive sets, 1 in the first, 1 more in the second, 1 more than that in the third set, etc. Without actually counting, pick up the set of 4. How did you know it was 4?
3. Divide the pebbles in two different ways (it is necessary to illustrate the two aspects of division). State in words the two problems giving rise to the two operations you have performed. Sharing – How many in an equal group? How many left over? How many children can have 3 each? Also devise problems giving rise to multiplication.
4. Simple materials and experiments involving their use are described below.

Length:
1. Two pencils of identical size and colour. Devise experiences to find out whether or not a child has grasped the concept of conservation of length.
2. A length of ribbon or string about one yard long. Share the ribbon among four children so that each has an equal share. Record this activity, first in words and then in symbols. Which aspect of division is this? (Fractional or sharing aspect of division.) How else could you ask this question?
3. Two lengths of ribbon or string of different colours, one about 10 inches long, the other about a yard long. How many short hair ribbons can you cut from the larger length? How much is left over? Record your result (a) in words (b) in symbols. Which aspect of division is this?

Capacity: A jug of water and a set of six identical small plastic glasses.
1. How many glasses can be filled (to within 1/2 inch of the top) from the jug? Which aspect of division is this?
2. Share a jug of water among four children. Which aspect of division is this?

Money: 25 pennies
Make up an assignment involving the use of the four operations. It should be possible to find the solutions to these problems by using the pennies.

Weight: Parcels (weighing an exact number of ounces – up to 16 ounces). Rice (about 1/2 lb.) Balance scales. Weights 1 ounce to 1 lb.
Prepare assignments involving the use of weights to illustrate the four operations.

Time: A clock with large hands. Egg timers. A calendar and radio or T.V. program guide. Devise experiences to find out whether or not the child has grasped the concept of time.

Determining an equal share of ribbon for each child

6-6. Working Sessions 8, 9 and 10

The second stage is the preparation of a topic
for pupils, spanning the age range 5 to 16. The
topics suggested are related to those investigated
at adult level during sessions 3 and 4. After
some discussion of the topic selected, open-ended
questions are devised by teachers working
in pairs. The materials necessary for solving these
problems are then collected. This section of the
workshop is begun in the afternoon so that the
teachers may *sleep on* their questions and may
bring whatever additional materials they require
from home. The groups are then paired and
each works the other's questions using the
materials provided. In this way each group covers
two topics thoroughly. Any differences of opinion
are hammered out during the final discussion
period and a good deal of mutual help is given over
the final framing of open-ended questions.

6-7. Working Sessions 11 and 12

In scheduling a program it is wise to allow some
time for adjustment. In this connection we have
allotted the first half of session 11. This time may
be necessary for some groups to complete
their work or to tackle special projects of particular
interest. It is also wise to use part of this time
to schedule whole-group activities, such as
appropriate films, guest lectures, panel or group
discussions, demonstration classes, etc.

Working Sessions 11 and 12 conclude the
first 3-day section of the workshop program. A
summary of mathematical ideas covered so far
(illustrated, where possible, by examples of
children's work) should be made. It is also important to use time in this session to clarify the
plans for the 6-week interval.

6-8. The 6-Week Interval

Each group of teachers from an area decide on a
topic to be tried out in their classrooms during
the six weeks between the workshops. We suggest
that these groups make plans to meet more than
once during the six weeks to discuss problems,
share ideas and prepare materials.

The plan drawn up by a group of teachers who
selected *perimeter* as their topic is shown on
page 88.

6-9. Working Sessions 13 and 14

In the second three-day section of the workshop,
the emphasis is shifted to extending the mathematical background of the teachers. An appropriate
title for this section might be "Patterns in Mathematics." As might be expected, teachers on the
second workshop seem to gravitate to their original
mixed groups.

Charts can be used to introduce the first unit,
"Patterns in Statistics." Materials for this unit are
calculating machines, tape measures, watches
with second hands and art supplies for making
charts (large sheets of 1" ruled paper, scissors,
coloured construction paper, marking pens, etc.).

Each teacher is given the enquiries shown on
page 89, asked to take his own measurements
(nearest whole numbers are used), and do the
necessary calculations to complete the form.
Metric measures can be used if desired.

PERIMETER

Grade Level	Aim	Open-end Questions
K - 2	Concept all the way around. Comparing Larger and Smaller Regular and Irregular shapes	How many things can you go around? In how many ways? How far is it around?
1 - 3	How far around?	In how many ways can we measure around? Which way is best? (easiest)
2 - 5	Estimating and Checking	How far do you think it is around any shapes you can measure?
	Real Measuring	See if you were right. How close were you?
	Large Perimeters	Find a way to draw a picture of your classroom floor so that others can tell its perimeter by measuring the picture.
3 - 6	Accuracy Symmetrical Figures	Can you find the perimeter of some shapes without measuring all the way around? Which shapes?
4 - 7	Scale	Make a scale drawing of your classroom or room at home.
5 - 8	Relationship - Perimeter Area	In what way can you arrange a fixed area to get the largest perimeter? Find the largest area (shape) you can enclose with a string one yard long.
	Relationship - Circumference Radius Area etc.	What is the relationship between area and perimeter? Can you find a relationship between the measurements of different circular objects?

PATTERNS IN STATISTICS

<u>Materials</u> for each table: 1 calculating machine, desk type; 2 tape measures; watch with
second hand at each table. 1 large sheet of 1" paper for each table. Scissors.

<u>Information</u> for each of the 9 questions is to be collected from each table on separate sheets
of paper. Some of the questions cannot be answered until the data is gathered.
(Answers - nearest whole number)

1. Number of children in the family in which you grew up (include yourself).
    Boys_____Girls_____
    Your position in family_____Sex_____
    What percentage of the teachers in this workshop are first born?_____

2. Waist in inches_____Weight in pounds_____Sex_____
    (Is there any relationship or correlation between waist and weight?)

3. Shoe size_____Sex_____

4. Height_____Reach (arms outstretched)_____Sex_____
    Are you a square? Compare the number of tall rectangles, squares and wide rectangles.

5. Estimate your skin area in square feet_____Sex_____
    Estimate your volume (not your capacity!) in pints_____
    How many square inches of skin have you for each pint of you?_____

6. Pulse rate sitting_____Pulse rate after running on the spot
    briskly for 30 seconds_____Sex_____

7. Area of your left foot in square inches_____
    Weight_____Sex_____Find the pressure on your feet in
    pounds per square inch when standing on both feet_____

8. Birthday month_____Day_____Sex_____
    How many birthday twins are there?_____

9. Your estimate of the height and length of this room in feet_____
    Height_____Length_____Sex_____

89

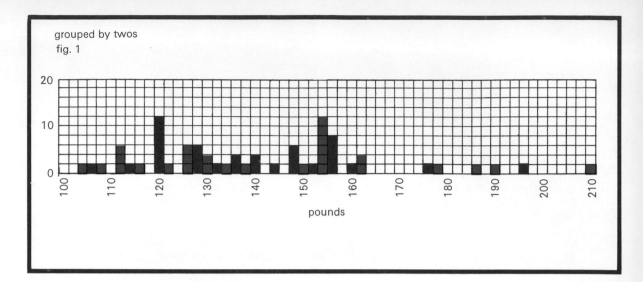

grouped by twos
fig. 1

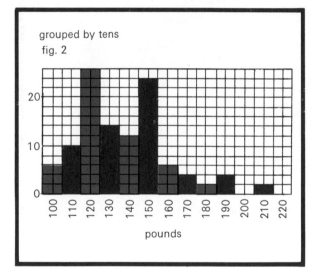

grouped by tens
fig. 2

The effect of grouping data

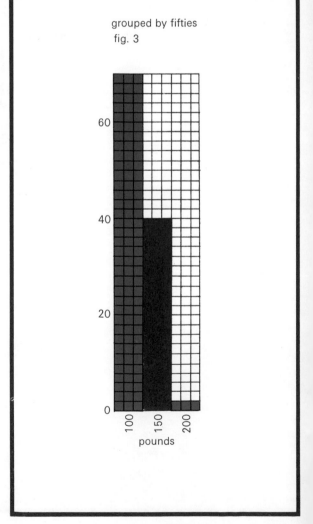

grouped by fifties
fig. 3

The information for each of the 9 enquiries
is transferred to separate sheets. Each sheet
is then passed to the group that has been asked
to plan and prepare the statistical chart for that
topic. An alternate plan is to cut up the completed
questionnaire and pass each enquiry to the proper
group.

Each of the groups was also given the following
instructions:

1/ Put the data in order. Represent the data by a
graph (you may need to *group* the data).
For example, individual weights could be recorded
on the chart; however, a more useful result
can be obtained if each weight is assigned to a
group (90-99, 100-109, 110-119, etc.). Grouping
scores causes a smoothing or masking of
individual differences, figure 1 and figure 2.
This can be carried too far, as you will discover if,
for example, you group the results in intervals
of 50 instead of 10 units, figure 3.

2/ Comment on the results obtained e.g.
Range of results
Central tendencies:
a/ The most popular value (mode)
b/ The middle value (median)
c/ The arithmetic mean. (Could you find this
by guessing some easy value — and compensating
afterwards?)
d/ High school teachers may like to work out
the mean deviation and the standard deviation.
Comment on the advantages and disadvantages
of each measure of central tendency.

3/ Is there a sex difference in the statistics?

4/ Find the size of the first random sample
which resembles the total population considered —
10? 25? 50? What is the easiest way to do this?
Would a block graph help?
How can you ensure that the samples you consider
are samples chosen at random?
Devise different methods of doing this.
How is sampling procedure used in industry?
In agriculture?

Sometimes it is necessary to furnish clues
to the teachers in order to expedite solutions.
The following is an example of how one tutor in a
group of teachers tackled enquiry number 5.

Using floor tile to estimate surface area

In this particular enquiry, skin area and volume
in pints, teachers were asked to give as careful
estimates as possible. They were encouraged
to take any rough measures and comparisons
which would help them to do this e.g. trace around
the body of a teacher lying on the floor and use
a square tile of side 12" to estimate the area.
To obtain their volume in pints they were asked:
"How many of you can float? How many sink?"
There were always some of each. "What does
this tell you about your density compared with
that of water?" At this stage someone usually
suggested that our density could not be very
different from that of water. "But how heavy is a

gallon of water?'' was the next question. Frequently there was no one at a particular table who knew this, so a quantity of water had to be weighed to find out. ''How much water will have to be weighed? Will a pint give a sufficiently accurate result to find the weight of a gallon of water? Which scales would it be best to use?'' were the next questions which arose. Once the approximate weight of a gallon of water was determined, calculation of each teacher's volume in pints was comparatively simple.

Tutors should encourage teachers to take an active part in ordering the raw scores collected for the charts. For many teachers this may be the first experience of ordering numerical data of this kind, more particularly of grouping data and observing the effect of this on histograms. For example, the chart on page 90 gives the weights of the teachers (1) as recorded by individuals, and (2) when each weight is assigned to a group.

The degree of accuracy appropriate for each measurement and the resulting calculations may cause the teachers some difficulty. As groups sort and order the data they will find that calculations must be made to different degrees of accuracy. To avoid cumbersome calculations at the beginning, measures were indicated in whole numbers; for example, waist measure in inches, area of footprint in square inches, weight in pounds, no half sizes in shoes. (It is amusing to notice that men usually approximate to a larger size — 10½ as 11 — whereas women quote the size smaller — 7½ as 7.) But in calculations such as the pressure on each square inch of foot, if results are given to the nearest pound, most people would have 2 or 3 pounds pressure per square inch, when standing on both feet. Here, an appropriate degree of accuracy can be obtained by giving the answer in pounds to one decimal place.

On the other hand, the calculations of the number of square inches of skin area to each pint provides numbers large enough for results to the nearest whole number to be appropriate. Teachers should refer to *appropriate degree of accuracy* and should understand that an absolute degree of accuracy is meaningless.

It should be pointed out to the teachers that in a small sample out-of-line data† can cause *skewing*. In this respect, perhaps the most

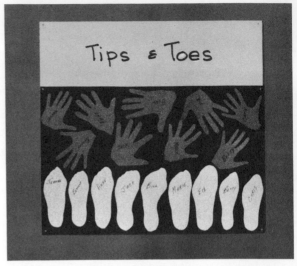

interesting of the investigations will be that showing the comparison between the estimate of the length and height of a room. Usually some teachers in the group will make estimates far out of line with the actual measures. The graph of this data will usually be skewed in proportion to the number of teachers making out-of-line guesses. The following graph is given so that tutors can discuss with teachers the possibility of rejecting out-of-line data when the sample is small.

As a contrast, each group might compare the results for everyone attending the workshop, with those found at its own table.

The meaning and relevance of the three measures of central tendency should be considered for each investigation. For example, in shoe sizes, the mode (most popular or most frequent size) is useful information for a manufacturer; so also is a knowledge of the frequency distribution of sizes. But the arithmetic mean or average has no meaning at all and the median or middle score of an ordered set of scores is not a useful piece of information. Teachers should realize that the range of the scores for any investigation is usually more informative than the arithmetic mean, although this is one bit of information that is usually required in statistics.

†By out-of-line data we mean unusual or abnormal data such as might result from wild guessing.

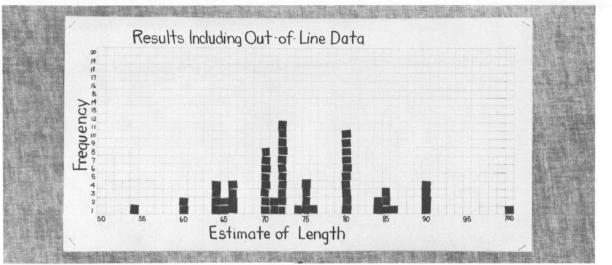

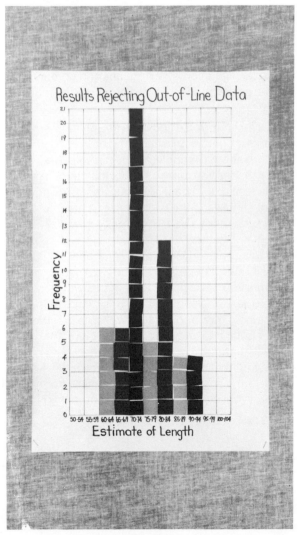

The effect of out-of-line data

Once again, the question of the distribution obtained when zero values are omitted from the axes should be discussed, for example, in a weight and waist correlation graph. It is often necessary to omit zero but in that event a small graph in which zero is included on both axes should be appended to the larger representation.

Some groups will be interested in *deviation* from the mean, and in standard deviation. We suggest that any teachers who would like to pursue this topic further for their own background consult an elementary book on statistics.

An alternate plan for secondary teachers and others who might be interested would be to provide a unit on probability.

Materials: 4 dice, 2 cups, 3 pennies.
Aim for at least 500 tries.
1/ Toss
a/ a penny   } repeatedly and record results
b/ 2 pennies   } in *order*. What do you notice
c/ 3 pennies   } about the results?

2/ Record scores in order using —
a/ 1 die
b/ 2 dice (total score)

It is interesting to compare the charts from the relatively small samples (at most 100 scores) with the larger samples (more than 500) used for the probability experiments.

6-10. Working Sessions 15 and 16

The afternoon is devoted to the exhibition of the pupils' work, accomplished during the six-week interval between the workshop sections. We feel the most effective way to exhibit pupils' materials is to have the teachers who investigated the same topic arrange their pupils' work in the same display area. By displaying pupils' work by *topic* rather than grade level, it is possible to see the stages of sophistication from the younger to older children. Two teachers should remain at each display to answer questions as the others view the exhibition. Opportunity should be given for general discussion of individual difficulties encountered during the 6-week interval.

Many teachers will feel that the 6-week interval has given them sufficient experience and confidence in the active learning approach; they now plan to incorporate active learning more fully in their teaching. Some teachers, however, will require advice about the further development of the work and *where to go next.*

6-11 Working Sessions 17 and 18

The unit for the second morning is "Patterns in Shapes." Assignment cards can be prepared and used to introduce this unit which covers three topics: symmetry, similarity and limits. Alternative questions on symmetry, including rotations of a square, may be provided for secondary teachers. Opportunity should be given for all teachers at the workshop to view and discuss the work of other groups. Materials and sample questions for assignment cards for the development of this unit are listed below.

Patterns in Shapes

Materials for each Table.
Patterned material or wallpaper patterns
3 small rectangular mirrors made to stand vertically
10 coloured inch squares, scissors, 4 coloured drafting pins
Sheets of plain paper: ¼" and ½" squared paper
12 sheets of coloured gummed 6" squares
Paint, brush
Cellulose tape
Sets of triangles and quadrilaterals made from bristol board or similar material: 15 congruent regular triangles in 3 colours; 15 congruent scalene triangles in 3 colours; 16 congruent quadrilaterals in 4 colours
Circular protractor
Cardboard strips (Described in Chapter 3 page 33)
Paper fasteners
60 coloured cubes

Materials to be Available. Kaleidoscopes. Cubes, rectangular boxes of various shapes and sizes. Balls of various sizes. Templates of regular pentagons, hexagons, octagons.

Developmental Questions for Symmetry

1/ Experiment with paint blots, squared paper, folded plain paper and scissors to see what you can discover about symmetry. How many different kinds of symmetry can you find? What correspondences can you discover? Use a mirror to help you. Find examples of congruence from the materials on this table (textiles, wallpaper patterns, leaves). By paper folding and cutting make familiar geometrical shapes and comment on the correspondences and properties you discover.

2/ What can you discover by fitting regular triangles together on a flat surface? What can you find out about the angles of the triangles and other shapes you make? Is there a pattern in the angle sum of the shapes? What can you discover about angles and the angle sum of a triangle when you make a pattern by fitting irregular triangles together?

Fold a square in half along a diagonal. What can you say about the sum of the angles of the triangle you have made? Repeat this with a rectangle. Is the angle sum of this folded triangle the same? Draw and cut out two large triangles, one regular and one irregular. Work with the regular triangle first; fold the corners over to bring them together so that you can discover the sum of the three angles. How did you make your folds? What else can you discover from this?

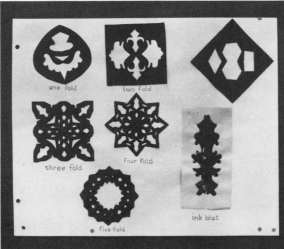

Symmetrical figures made by folding and cutting paper and by ink blots

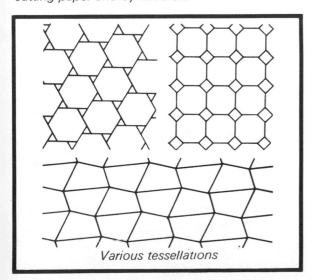

Various tessellations

3/ Make a set of shapes using the shortest cardboard strips of equal length and using one more strip each time. Which shape is rigid? What do you have to do to make the other shapes rigid? (Keep your shapes flat on the table). How many variables are there in your set of shapes? What patterns do you notice? Make tables and graphs to illustrate the patterns and relationships you discover. (Include the pattern of the angle sum of successive shapes, interior angles, exterior angles. What happens when the number of strips becomes very large?)

4/ Use equilateral triangles to form a regular hexagon. Does this suggest a way of constructing a set of regular polygons with 7,8,9, etc. sides? With any number of sides? Can you discover a relationship between the angle at the centre of each polygon and the number of sides the polygon has? Make a table for these two variables and illustrate this by a graph. What happens when the number of sides becomes very large? What is the relationship between a centre angle and the number of sides the polygon has?

5/ Which shapes would be of use for measuring area? Try with congruent regular shapes first — then with congruent irregular shapes. Guess first whether you can *tile* with each shape before you try to fit the tiles together. Can you justify your results?

Why do bees use hexagonal cells? Use the regular shapes to make 3-dimensional models. How many variables are there? Can you find any relationships?

6/ Experiment with boxes and find out in how many ways you can replace the lids. Can you discover anything about the symmetries of the different shapes from your experiments?

7/ Which capital letters, geometrical shapes and other shapes can you cut from a piece of folded paper (a) folded in two (b) folded in four? In how many ways can you put these shapes back into the openings from which they were cut? Experiment using parallel folds of paper.

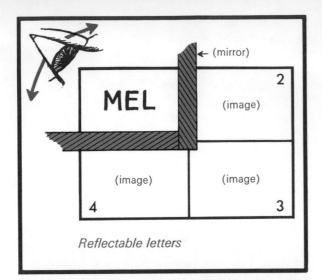

Reflectable letters

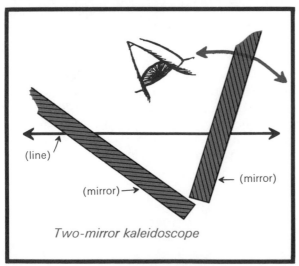

Two-mirror kaleidoscope

8/a/ Write your name in block letters in box 1. Draw what you see in the other three boxes if the mirrors are arranged as shown in the diagram. Experiment with capital letters and see if you you can find a *reflectable* word.

b/ Reflect two intersecting lines. Use one mirror to see if you can get regular geometrical shapes.

c/ Make a kaleidoscope using *two mirrors*. What happens as the angle changes? Can you discover a relationship? Experiment using first a single object (e.g. a pin with coloured head) and secondly a line segment with an end on each mirror. Make a table and a graph of your results. (It is easier to consider the total number of objects you can see; that is, real and images.)

d/ What does a letter F look like after one reflection in each of two mirrors which meet at an angle? Is the result always the same?

What happens if the mirrors are parallel? Which letters are the same after any number of reflections? Describe and explain some reflection situations in everyday life.

9/ Use tracing paper to find which letters look the same upside down. Do any of these letters look unchanged in a mirror? Draw or trace an S. In how many ways can you put the tracing back on the original without turning the tracing over? After turning the tracing over? Which letters seem to turn into other letters when you turn the paper over or around? (No wonder reading is hard for some children!)

10/ Draw and trace (or map) a shape. What do you discover about corresponding distances and angles?

Movement in a plane without distortion can be brought about in three ways:

By reflection in an axis in the plane.

By rotation about an axis at right angles to the plane. Rotational symmetry is familiar in natural forms (e.g. flowers, snowflakes) and in man-made forms. This is sometimes called S symmetry. The angle of rotation is usually quite easily seen. If not, the basic shape can be traced and then rotated about a pin through the centre of symmetry until the basic shape coincides with the repetitions of this shape. Investigate

the symmetrical properties of an equilateral triangle, a rhombus, a parallelogram, a five-pointed star, a hexagon, and the letters of the alphabet. Which shapes occur most frequently in nature?

By translation or movement sideways, upwards or both. Translation is used in the familiar repeating patterns of wallpapers or room dividers. What is the distance between each pattern? Is this the same in each pattern?

Developmental Questions for Similarity

1/ Use small cubes to make larger cubes. How many variables are there in your sequence of cubes? *(edge length, surface area, volume)* Make tables and illustrate by graphs. What is the relationship of surface area to volume? What does a graph show? Repeat this experiment with identical cuboids (right rectangular prisms) to make larger cuboids. Do you get the same result?

2/ Which of the following sets of shapes are always similar? Can you say under what conditions the sets of other shapes would be similar? Cubes, spheres, cones, cuboids, cylinders, squares, rectangles, circles, rhombuses, parallelograms, quadrilaterals, regular hexagons, equilateral triangles, isosceles triangles.

3/ How many small balls would occupy the same space as the large ball? Make a careful estimate first. (Choose 2 balls with diameters in an easy ratio e.g. 1 to 2 or 1 to 3. The purpose is to see whether the concept has been grasped, not to give tiresome calculations.)

4/ Using similar containers, determine how many small containers it would take to fill a large container. Estimate first, then make comparisons to improve your estimate. Check your result.

Developmental Questions for Limits

1/ Place a loop of string, 12 inches long, around a drawing pin or thumbtack. What shape can you trace out with a pencil, keeping the string taut? What shape do you trace out when you use two drawing pins? How can you vary this shape using the same loop of string? What is the largest shape you can trace out? What is the smallest shape? Illustrate your answer. Now try this with 3 drawing pins.

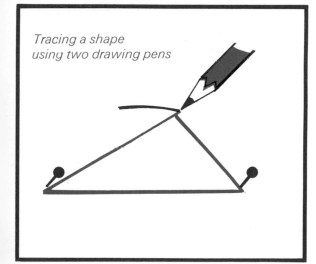

*Tracing a shape
using two drawing pens*

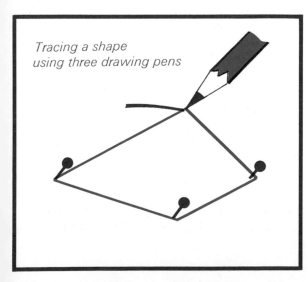

*Tracing a shape
using three drawing pens*

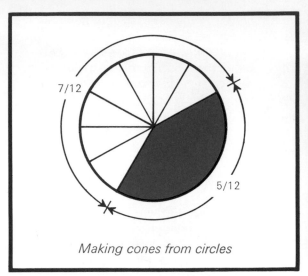

7/12

5/12

Making cones from circles

To Find WHAT HAPPENS TO THE VOLUME IF WE CUT CONES FROM DIFFERENT SECTORS OF THREE-INCH CIRCLES.

2/ Draw a large square on a sheet of ¼" squared paper. Find the mid-points of each side of the square and join successive mid-points. What is the new shape? Can you justify your suggestion? Continue, finding and joining the mid-points of each successive shape. What relationships can you discover? Describe carefully what will eventually happen as you continue this process. Is there a limit? Can you reverse the process to make a larger square than your original one? How far can you go?

3/ Repeat, using a rectangle, a rhombus, and any quadrilateral. What interesting properties do you discover? Repeat, using (1) a regular triangle (2) a scalene triangle.

4/ Extend this pattern ← 2, 4, 8, 16, 32, → in both directions. Is there a lower limit? An upper limit?

5/ Find the sum of the exterior angles of a regular triangle, a square, a hexagon, and octagon. What do you discover? Use this fact to find the exterior angle of each of the regular shapes: triangle, square, pentagon, hexagon. Continue to 20 sides, 120 sides, 360 sides, 3600 sides. What do you notice about the exterior angle of a regular polygon as the number of its sides increases? Illustrate your answer by a graph. Is there an upper limit to the size of the exterior angle? What does your graph show? (Ought the graph to be a continuous line?) Is there a lower limit?

6/ Is there a relationship between the number of sides a regular polygon has and its interior angle? Illustrate your answer by a table and a graph. What would be the interior angle of a polygon with 36, 360 or 3600 sides? Is there an upper limit? A lower limit? What does your graph show?

7/ To make a set of 10 cones, cut out 6 circles each with a radius of 3 inches. Using a protractor, divide each circle into 12 equal pie-shaped sections. Remove one section from the first circle and glue the larger part together to form the first cone. With the second circle remove 2 sections. Join each of these two parts to make 2 additional cones. Proceed in this manner, making 2 cones from each circle. (Note, although you can make two cones from the last circle, they will be identical.) What are the upper and lower limits of the set of cones? What are the upper and lower limits of the volume of the cones? Illustrate any interesting relationships you discover.

8/ The area of each of a set of rectangles is 12 square inches. Sketch the complete set considering the integral values only for the sides. Next, assuming fractional values may be used for the sides, complete the following table:

width in inches	1	½	¼	⅛	1/16
length in inches	12				

Describe what is happening to these rectangles. Is there a limit to this sequence? Illustrate by a graph.

9/ Can you find the pattern and continue this sequence (to 12 pairs)?

1	1		1	
1	2			.5
2	3	.667		
3	5			.6
–	–			
–	–			

As you discover each new ordered pair, write the ratio of the first number to the second (to 3 decimal places) arranging these alternately on one side and the other of the vertical line. What do you discover? Is there a limit? Represent these ordered pairs on a graph and comment on your result.

10/ Construct a regular pentagon. Join alternate vertices. What new shape is formed? Continue, joining alternate vertices. What is happening? Is there a limit? Can you discover any relationships? Has this any connection with the previous question?

6-12. Working Session 19

The first hour after lunch is spent on "Patterns in Graphs." This lesson, a paper and pencil exercise, is designed to cover the range of practical work accomplished in previous sessions. It is intended to extend or refresh the background of elementary teachers, and to suggest for secondary teachers an approach to teaching algebraic graphs and relationships through patterns. Teachers should be encouraged to work in pairs with one partner working out the pattern and the other drawing small graphs to illustrate the relationship. Many teachers will complete about three-quarters of the questions which follow. The last section on vectors is primarily designed for secondary school teachers.

Instructions for Patterns in Graphs

Select several experiments and use the following directions to interpret the results. Using integers, make a table to show a relation between the variables and note the pattern as the variables change. Sketch a graph (discrete integral points) to illustrate this pattern. Is it *meaningful* to draw a *smooth curve through the points?* Comment on the pattern by which the one variable changes for equal changes in the other variable. Describe the relation between the variables.

1/ Multiplication Tables: Illustrate the relation $P = 2n$ (the 2-times table) by a table, then by a graph. Generalize this for the 3-times table and so on. It is conventional to use the horizontal axis for the variable n.

2/ Find the dimension of each rectangle with a constant perimeter of 12 inches. Let w, l and p represent the measures in inches of the width, length and perimeter respectively.

$P = 12$

w	l

Complete the table, then graph the relation between w and l; that is, the set of ordered pairs (w,l).

3/ Find the area, A square inches, of each rectangle with a constant perimeter of 12 inches.

$P = 12$

w	l	A

Complete the table, then graph the relation between w and A; that is, the set of ordered pairs (w,A). Express by a formula the relation between w and A.

4/ Find the perimeter, P in inches, of a square with sides of length s inches, when $s = 1, 2, 3, 4, 5, 6$.

s	P

Complete the table and graph (s,P).

Compare this relation with (d,c) where d and c are the diameter and circumference of a circle. Let $d = 1, 2, 3, 4, 5, 6$. Complete the table and graph (d,c).

d	c

5/ Find the area, A square inches, of a square with sides of length s inches, where $s = 1, 2, 3, 4, 5, 6$. Discuss the pattern by which A changes as s increases. Compare (s,A) with (s,P) of experiment 4, and graph (s,A). Compare (s,A) with the relation between the diameter and area of a circle (d,A).

6/ Find the width, length and perimeter of each rectangle with area 36 square inches.

$A = 36$

w	l	P

Graph (w,l)
Graph (w,P)
Discuss the pattern for each graph as w increases.

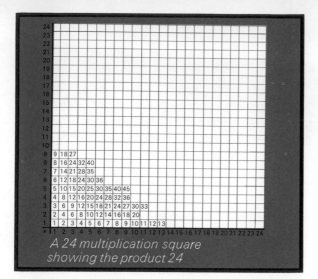

A 24 multiplication square
showing the product 24

7/ Make a multiplication square (using ½ inch square paper), and label the squares 1,2,3,....,24 along the bottom and up the left side as shown in the diagram.

a/ Without completing the table, colour in red all squares that would contain the product 24. Sketch a curve to pass through the centres of the squares containing the product 24. Compare this with the graphs in experiment 6. Explain the similar nature of the shapes of these graphs. Is it meaningful to join these centres?

b/ Repeat the above procedure for the product 36.

c/ Label the horizontal axis the x — axis, and the vertical axis the y — axis and draw the graph, in the first quadrant, of $xy = 24$ in red and of $xy = 36$ in blue. Is it meaningful to draw a smooth curve through the points? What relation exists between the co-ordinates of each point on the curve?

8/ Draw a sequence of regular polygons, beginning with a square. Starting with one vertex, draw lines (diagonals) to each of the remaining vertices. Assuming the sum of the angles of a triangle is two right angles, find all the relationships you can concerning number of sides (n), number of diagonals (d), number of triangles (t) formed by the diagonals, and the sum of angles (E) of the triangles formed.

9/ Find the relationship between the number of sides of a regular polygon and its exterior angle, and the relationship between the interior and exterior angles of any regular polygon.

10/ Find the volumes of a set of cubes with edges 1, 2, 3, 4, 5, 6 (in inches). Find the number pattern and graph the set of ordered pairs (s,V). How do the volumes of the cubes compare with those for a set of balls with diameters 1, 2, 3, 4, 5, 6 (in inches)?

The following experiments are somewhat more difficult; however (allowing for experimental error), each gives various mathematic relationships. It often helps to consider values of zero or those near zero.

11/ In how many ways can you vary the swing of a pendulum? By changing one variable at a time, see what relationships you can discover.

12/ Run a truck on a track down a long incline (e.g. a balance form). What are the variables? See if you can find a relationship between distance covered and time, then a relationship between weight carried and time.

13/ Can you find any relationship by dropping a ball from different heights?

14/ Can you find a relationship between the weight in air of a set of stones and their weight in water?

15/ Can you find a relationship between the stretch of a spring or piece of elastic and the weight added?

Summary/ The relationships of examples 1 to 15 can be summarized in the following table. Enter the relations you have discovered in the appropriate column in the table.

Cubes $y = x^3$	Squares $y = x^2$	Straight Line $y = x$	Straight Line $y = 1$	Constant Product $xy = 1$ $(y = \frac{1}{x}, x \neq 0)$

Vectors. Vectors occur in many branches of mathematics as measures of quantities involving both magnitude and direction, such as velocity, force and displacement.

1/ What is the sum of two vectors? We say that the set of all vectors is closed under vector addition. Why do we say this?

2/ Find $(3,4) + (1,2)$[†] and compare with $(1,2) + (3,4)$. What do you discover? Try several more examples to verify your results. If all other results verify the first, does this prove the relationship?

3/ Find $(\overrightarrow{AB} + \overrightarrow{BC}) + \overrightarrow{CA}$ and $\overrightarrow{AB} + (\overrightarrow{BC} + \overrightarrow{CA})$

4/ With and without drawing find the vector equivalent to
$(1,3) + (2,5) + (^-3,^-3)$.
$(0,0)$ is called the zero vector.

5/ Start with vector $(2,3)$. What vector will bring you back to the initial point, the origin? $(^-2,^-3)$ is called the inverse of $(2,3)$. The inverse of $\overrightarrow{OA}$ is $\overrightarrow{AO}$.

6/ Summarize the results of 1 to 5 by stating properties of the set of all vectors in a plane.

6-13. Working Session 20 and part of 21

As in sessions 8, 9 and 10, members of the course choose and develop a topic on shapes that they would be interested in developing for children. The list of topics includes proportion, ratio, tessellations (tiling), inequalities, symmetry, similarity, pattern, three-dimensional shapes, limits and growth. We suggest each teacher sign his name and record the grade level he teaches under the topic of his choice. Each table can then be organized according to the topic chosen. If possible, group teachers together representing different grade levels. No more than two tables should be permitted to develop the same topic.

The first task of each group is to decide on the progression or development of the topic from the age 5 to 16. This should be recorded and left at the table for one of the other groups to discuss and comment on. Then comes the challenge

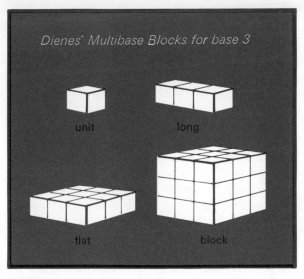

Dienes' Multibase Blocks for base 3

unit   long

flat   block

of preparing open-ended questions for each grade level. Teachers usually select and write questions for the age range with which they have had the most experience. We strongly suggest that teachers be allowed to think about this overnight in order that they may come the next day with whatever additional equipment or materials they will need. Once the problems and materials are organized, groups can exchange tables and examine the development of the topic and the open-ended questions. The real value of this session is in the preliminary discussions and the preparation of the questions.

6-14. Working Sessions 21 and 22

The next session should be spent on the topics "Patterns in Numbers," (p. 103), "Patterns in Sets" (pp. 104 and 105), and "Patterns in Algebra." We have also included material of a more difficult nature for secondary teachers — "Patterns in Numbers 2" (p. 107), and "Patterns in Groups."

We suggest that *Dienes' Multibase Arithmetic Blocks* or similar material be provided for each table. Dienes' Blocks are made in bases 3, 4, 5, 6 and 10. Each base consists of a number of units, longs, flats and blocks. A unit is a cubic centimetre of hardwood. The others are multiples of the base unit. For example, in base 3 there are the materials shown in the figure above.

[†] The co-ordinates used in these exercises refer to the terminal point of the position vector. For more information see M. E. Shanks and others, *Pre-Calculus Mathematics* (Menlo Park, California, Addison-Wesley Publishing Co., Inc., 1965) and H. A. Elliott and others, *Geometry in the Classroom* (Toronto, Holt, Rinehart and Winston of Canada, Ltd., 1968).

Each group is asked to discover the relationships between the four different pieces of apparatus. The teachers in each group work in pairs to study the four operations of addition, subtraction, multiplication and division. In working sessions 7 and 8 teachers probably found that both aspects of division and subtraction occurred earlier and more frequently than addition and multiplication. Now, using the Dienes' structural material, they are asked to work through the operations in the usual order. In subtraction the teachers should find different ways of asking questions which lead to building up (complementary addition) and breaking down (decomposition or regrouping). In division they are asked to discover why, in written calculation, we normally begin with the left hand figure. It is in the manipulation of materials that the notion of *remainder* takes on real meaning.

The assignments from the following pages are given to the teachers. Special provision should be made for secondary teachers to develop activities in finite arithmetic or activities on groups.

Patterns in Algebra

If pupils are encouraged to look for patterns, they can sometimes discover algebraic properties that they might not understand if these properties are presented to them in a traditional manner.

1/ Find the pattern in each of the following ordered sets of numbers and continue the pattern in both directions:

a/ $\{-, -, -, 10, 100, 1000, 10000, -, -\}$
$\{-, -, -, 10^1, 10^2, 10^3, 10^4, -, -\}$

b/ $\{-, -, -, 2, 4, 8, 16, -, -\}$
$\{-, -, -, 2^1, 2^2, 2^3, 2^4, -, -\}$

c/ $\{-, -, -, 3, 9, 27, -, -, -\}$
$\{-, -, -, 3^1, 3^2, 3^3, -, -, -\}$

Compare the sets in (a), (b) and (c). How would you describe each of these sets?

2/ What can you discover by finding successive differences between the terms of the following sequences?

a/ $\qquad$ $-, 4, -, 8, -, 12, -, -, -, ...$
Differences $-, -, (4), -, (4), -, -, -, -, ...$
Differences $-, -, -, (0), -, -, -, -, -, ...$

b/ $\qquad$ $-, 1, -, 4, -, 9, -, 16, -, ...$
Differences $-, -, (3), -, (5), -, (7), -, -, ...$
Differences $-, -, -, (2), -, (2), -, -, -, ...$
Differences $-, -, -, -, (0), -, -, -, -, ...$

c/ Repeat with the above pattern for
$0, 1, 8, 27, 64, -, -, ...$.

Describe the sequences in (a), (b) and (c). Ask secondary teachers to write down the $(n-1)^{th}, n^{th},$ and $(n+1)^{th}$ terms in each sequence in order to emphasize the general algebraic pattern.

3/ Pupils accustomed to using a number line when discussing the whole numbers can be encouraged to try the operations when the number line is used to represent integers. (Some students will do this of their own accord when the number line is first extended to include negative numbers.)

$$\longleftarrow \quad ^-7 \ ^-6 \ ^-5 \ ^-4 \ ^-3 \ ^-2 \ ^-1 \ 0 \ ^+1 \ ^+2 \ ^+3 \ ^+4 \ ^+5 \ ^+6 \ ^+7 \ ^+8 \quad \longrightarrow$$

Use the number line (for integers) to solve the following examples. Establish rules (definitions) for addition, subtraction, multiplication and division with two integers.

Addition:
$^+3 + {}^+4 = \square \ ; {}^+4 + {}^+3 = \square$
$^+3 + {}^-4 = \square \ ; {}^-4 + {}^+3 = \square$
$^+4 + {}^-4 = \square \ ; {}^-4 + {}^+4 = \square$

Subtraction: (the inverse of addition)
$^+6 - {}^+2 = \square$ $\qquad$ How far is it from $^+2$ to $^+6$?
$\qquad$ or, What must I add to $^+2$ to get $^+6$?
$\qquad$ (i.e. $^+2 + \square = {}^+6$)
$^+6 - {}^-2 = \square$ $\qquad$ How far is it from $^-2$ to $^+6$?
$\qquad$ or, What must I add to $^-2$ to get $^+6$?
$\qquad$ (i.e. $^-2 + \square = {}^+6$)
$^-3 - {}^-2 = \square$ $\qquad$ $^-2 + \square = {}^-3$
$^-3 - {}^+2 = \square$ $\qquad$ $^+2 + \square = {}^-3$

(con't. on p. 106)

PATTERNS IN NUMBER

1. a. Using Dienes' Blocks, discover relationships between units, longs, flats and blocks. Express the sum of the Dienes' Blocks you have taken in several ways. (You may find that children use other names such as cubes, squares, rods, units.) What is the value or sum of the Dienes' Blocks of both you and your partner?

b. Which of you has more? Show how much more in <u>wood</u>. How else could you ask questions which would lead your students to subtraction? (What is the difference? What must I add to one to make the other? Take the smaller from the larger, etc.) Now try a more formal subtraction using material.

	Blocks	Flats	Longs	Units
From	1	2	2	1
Subtract		1	1	2
(Base 3 -	1	1	0	2)

2. Take any amount of Dienes' Blocks, ensuring that you have at least one of each type. Double this amount. Record the original amount and multiply by the base number. For example, if you have base 4, what would 4 times your original amount be? What pattern do you notice? Compare this with multiplication by base 10.

3. Using Dienes' Blocks, try both aspects of division. Where did you begin? Can you discover why, in division, we normally begin with the left hand end (the largest number)?

4. How could you use an abacus to give children experience in working with other bases? How could 2 children play a dice game in base 3? Devise your own rules.

5. a. Use a set of weights: 1oz, 2oz, 4oz, 8oz, 16oz, 32oz, 64oz (kitchen weights), to make a binary number table. Find the patterns in the binary number table. Use this table to convert, work and check the following problems:
7+5, 7x5, 16-11, 36÷9

64	32	16	8	4	2	1		Weight of Package in Ounces
						1	1	
					1	0	2	
					1	1	3	
				1	0	0	4	
				1	0	1	5	
				1	1	0	6	
				1	1	1	7	
			1	0	0	0	8	
			.	.	.	.	.	
			.	.	.	.	.	
			.	.	.	.	.	

OUNCES

b. Find the minimum sequence of weights which would be required to weigh parcels of whole numbers of ounces only, if you could use the weights on either side of the balance scales (i.e. on the opposite side to the parcel or on the same side as the parcel). Discover the patterns of this sequence.

Patterns in Sets

1. What can you say about the numbers in the set shown in fig.1? (Many answers possible, e.g. the set contains both odd and even numbers.) In how many ways can you partition these numbers into two subsets? (fig.2 and fig.3)

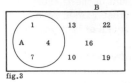

fig.1 fig.2 fig.3

Set <u>A</u> is_____. Set <u>B</u> is_____. Illustrate your answers.

2. Arrange 4 objects from your pocket or handbag on a sheet of paper (this defines your universal set). Use a loop of string to divide these objects into two subsets. Describe these. In how many ways can you divide the 4 objects into two subsets? **(16)**

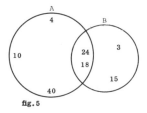

fig.4

3. Find four types or kinds of <u>sameness;</u> each type will allow you to separate the universal set into two subsets. Can you use two or more different types of sameness at the same time? Describe each subset carefully. Fig.4 shows the universal set for this problem.

4. What have the numbers in each circle in common? (see fig.5) What have the numbers in the overlap in common?

fig.5

5. Draw diagrams to represent the universal set of whole numbers less than 17, the subset <u>A</u> of the multiples of 4, and the subset <u>B</u> of the squares of the whole numbers. Combine the three diagrams.

The universal set for questions 6 to 8 is the set of whole numbers 20 to 40 inclusive.

6. List set $\underline{A}$, the subset of even numbers.
   List set $\underline{B}$, the subset of square numbers.
   List the set of numbers which are elements of both set $\underline{A}$ and set $\underline{B}$, (that is the intersection of sets $\underline{A}$ and $\underline{B}$).

7. List set $\underline{C}$, the subset of numbers divisible by 4.
   List set $\underline{D}$, the subset of prime numbers.
   List the set of numbers which are elements of both sets $\underline{C}$ and $\underline{D}$ (the intersection of sets $\underline{C}$ and $\underline{D}$).

8. List set $\underline{F}$, the subset of numbers divisible by 5.
   List set $\underline{G}$, the subset of numbers divisible by 3.
   List the intersection of $\underline{F}$ and $\underline{G}$.

9. Shade in the regions, if any, that represent the intersections of (a) set $\underline{X}$ and set $\underline{Y}$ (b) set $\underline{A}$ and set $\underline{B}$ (c) set $\underline{P}$ and set $\underline{Q}$.

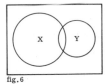 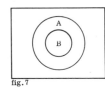 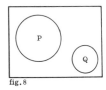

fig.6   fig.7   fig.8

In many textbooks you will find the union of set $\underline{A}$ and set $\underline{B}$ written $\underline{A} \cup \underline{B}$. The intersection of set $\underline{A}$ and set $\underline{B}$ may be written $\underline{A} \cap \underline{B}$.

The universal set E for questions 10 to 14 is the set of whole numbers 1 to 100 inclusive. (You might use a 100 square to represent $\underline{E}$.)

10. List $\underline{A}$, the subset of even whole numbers less than 20.
    List $\underline{B}$, the subset of square whole numbers less than 20.
    List the set of numbers in set $\underline{A}$ or in set $\underline{B}$ or both.
    List the set of numbers in set $\underline{A}$ and set $\underline{B}$.

11. List $\underline{C}$, the subset of whole numbers less than 30 divisible by 5.
    List $\underline{D}$, the subset of whole numbers less than 30 divisible by 3.
    List the set of numbers in set $\underline{C}$ or in set $\underline{D}$ or in both.
    List the set of numbers in set $\underline{C}$ and set $\underline{D}$.

12. List F, the subset of even whole numbers between 90 and 100.
    List G, the subset of odd whole numbers between 90 and 100.
    List the set of numbers in set F or in set G or in both.
    List the set of numbers in set F and in set G.

13. $\underline{M}_2$ is the subset of even numbers.
    $\underline{M}_4$ is the subset of multiples of 4.
    $\underline{M}_2 \cap \underline{M}_4$

14. Find other interesting relationships concerning the union and intersection of subsets $\underline{M}_2 \cup \underline{M}_3$ (multiples of 3) $\underline{M}_4 \cap \underline{M}_6$ etc.

Multiplication:

$+3 \times +2 = \square$ Take this to mean 3 times $+2$ (i.e. 3 steps of $+2$).

$+3 \times -2 = \square$ What does this mean to be consistent with the above?

What meaning should be given to $-3 \times +2$ in order that the commutative property will hold? We want the same result as for $+2 \times -3$.

$-3 \times +2 = \square$

Compare the results for $+3 \times -2$ and $-3 \times +2$.
What meaning should be given to -2×-3?
To find out, complete the following:

$+3 \times -3 = \square$	$0 \times -3 = \square$
$+2 \times -3 = \square$	$-1 \times -3 = \square$
$+1 \times -3 = \square$	$-2 \times -3 = \square$

Division: (the inverse of multiplication)

$+12 \div +3 = \square$ What must I multiply $+3$ by to get $+12$?
(i.e. $+3 \times \square = +12$)

$-12 \div +3 = \square$ What must I multiply $+3$ by to get -12?
(i.e. $+3 \times \square = -12$)

$-10 \div -2 = \square$	$-2 \times \square = -10$
$+18 \div -3 = \square$	$-3 \times \square = +18$

4/ Many mathematical truths do not seem sensible to children unless they have arrived at these for themselves. An appeal to pattern usually helps. Consider the following: Some of the following *sentences* are true, some are false, some are open. You can make a true or false sentence from an open sentence by replacing the variable(s) by numbers.

a/ Write T (true), F (false)

$1/2 + 1/2 = 1$	$2 \times 1/2 = 1$
$1/2 \times 1/2 = 1$	$2 \div 1/2 = 1$
$1/2 \div 1/2 = 1$	$2 + 1/2 = 1$
$1/2 - 1/2 = 1$	$2 - 1/2 = 1$
$2/2 = 1$	

Rewrite the false sentences so that they will be true.

b/ Find truth sets or solution sets for the following open sentences and represent each by a table, then by a graph (include negative numbers).

1. $\square + \triangle = 12$
2. $\square + \square = \triangle$
3. $\square \times \triangle = 24$
4. $\triangle = \square \times \square$
5. $\triangle = 3 \times \square$
6. $\triangle = \square \times \square \times \square$
7. $\square \times \square - 5 \square + 6 = 0$
8. $\square \times \square - 7 \square + 12 = 0$
9. $\square \times \square - 2 \square - 24 = 0$
10. $10x^2 - 23x + 12 = 0$

Patterns in Groups (Secondary)

Group structures arise in many different aspects of mathematics. You may have already studied some isomorphic groups of order 4.

Patterns in shapes (Rotation of a square)
Patterns in numbers (Finite arithmetic modular 4)
Patterns in graphs (Vectors)

The following are more examples of isomorphic groups of order 4. Check each for the four necessary conditions that a set must have to form a group under addition.

Any two elements combine to form a third which is a member of the set.

The associative law holds.

There is an identity element which has the property $a \circ i = i \circ a = a$ (o stands for the operation considered).

Each element has a unique inverse which combines with it to give the identity element.

1/ *Algebra* – Complex numbers. Test the operation of addition for the set $(1, i, -1, -i)$. Make an addition table.

2/ *Arithmetic* – Test each of the 4 simple operations (addition, subtraction, multiplication and division) for the set $(-3, -1, 1, 3)$. Make a table for each operation. What conclusions can you reach about each operation?

All teachers should spend the last three-quarters of an hour on "Patterns in Algebra." This unit was compiled from a list of topics which teachers said they found difficult to present to students when using discovery techniques. The exercises which follow are an attempt to encourage discovery by an appeal to pattern.

Patterns in Number 2 (Secondary)

Finite Arithmetic

1. Ask a group sitting around a table to number off in modulo 5. Use Cuisenaire or Colour Factor rods (colours represented by numbers 1 to 5) and give these out in order. Ask questions to develop the properties of a finite arithmetic modulo 5.

2. Find the effect of combining or adding two numbers of the set modulo 4; 0, 1, 2, 3. When the addition is 4 or more enter the <u>remainder</u> in the table. Complete the table and answer the questions using the table.

2nd

+	0	1	2	3
0	0	1	2	3
1			3	0
2				
3				

1st

3. Do any two elements combine to form a third which is also an element of the set?

4. Does the associative law hold?   (1+2) + 3 = ?   1 + (2 + 3) = ?

5. Is there an identity element; that is, an element which when added to another element leaves it unchanged?

6. Has each element a unique inverse? (Which element must be added to 3 to give 0? to 2?)

7. Make a multiplication table and test to see if it is a group.

6-15. Working Sessions 23 and 24

The final afternoon should be spent in summarizing the mathematics which has been attempted during the full workshop period. Examples of children's work can be used to illustrate the various topics. Considerable time should be devoted to a discussion of questions raised by the participants in the course on such problems as ways of encouraging colleagues to make a start, organizing the classroom and informing parents of the aims and methods of active learning. These problems have been presented and possible solutions offered in other chapters of this book.

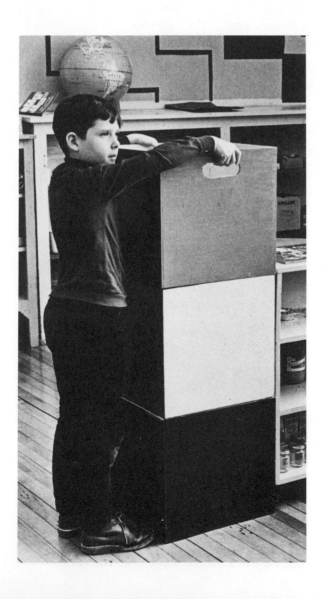

Chapter 7

Mathematics and Related Activities for Primary Grades

7-1	Topics of Counting	111
7-2	Addition, Subtraction, Multiplication and Division	117
7-3	Length	121
7-4	Perimeter and Area	127
7-5	Volume and Capacity	131
7-6	Time and Speed	134
7-7	Geometry—Shapes	139
7-8	Pictorial Representation, Block or Column Graphs	139

Mathematics and Related Activities for Primary Grades

In the next two chapters we shall consider the development of mathematics as one aspect of the curriculum. We hope that these chapters will help teachers and future teachers to plan the work of their classrooms and will help principals to plan the work of the school. We envisage the topics considered here as occurring repeatedly through-out the student's school life. Some topics may occur more frequently than others. Every time a familiar topic is encountered it should be studied in a more mature way at a higher level than on the previous occasion.

Some of the topics will be worked out in more detail than others. From time to time children's work will be included to focus attention on the difficulties and successes that children encounter. Classroom teachers will need to co-operate amongst themselves as well as with the principal to ensure that the mathematical education of each child is balanced and sufficiently challenging.

7-1. Topics of Counting

Initially, the most important concepts needed by children are those of counting and related topics. Without a thorough understanding of these topics children will not have the firm foundation necessary for further study in mathematics. Here especially, children should be involved in active learning. They need a multisensory, individualized approach.

Matching, One-to-One Correspondence, Counting

Children have various experiences of matching before they come to school: setting the table, usually with no one at the table; dressing, buttons and button holes; sharing sweets; etc. These experiences should be continued and extended in school. Comparing the number of objects in two sets, cups to saucers, is preliminary experience for counting. It is the recognition that sets of 4 toys, 4 cups, 4 books and 4 pencils have one character-istic in common – fourness – and these sets can be matched one-to-one or object-by-object. Counting is essentially giving a number name to each object of a set in order to find the cardinal number of the set. Therefore you must provide real objects for children to handle so that they can move each object as they say a number name. Care must be taken to ensure that children understand that although the *order* of saying the number names is important, the particular assignment of names to objects is not. This point may be illustrated by the following story.

A young boy was counting 5 pieces of candy. He picked each up in turn saying "1, 2, 3, 4, 5." Accidentally, the parent knocked 2 of the pieces onto the floor. Seeing this he asked the boy, "How many pieces of candy do you have now?" The boy replied, "1, 2, 5," again picking each piece up in turn. The helpful parent then told the child that he had three pieces of candy: "1, 2, 3." The boy, now quite upset with his parent, said, "3 is on the floor."

Similarly, children often confuse the cardinal and ordinal aspects of a number. A child who had counted out 5 blocks was asked to show the set of 5 to his teacher. He picked up the last block he had counted and said, "Five." He had not yet distinguished the fifth object counted in a sequence from the recognition of 5 objects in a set.

Conservation of Number

Once a child can count a set of objects without difficulty, it is necessary to find out whether he understands the concept of conservation of number. The number of objects in a set remains the same no matter how the objects are arranged within the set. This is quite easily checked. Take, for example, 8 cups and 6 saucers. Ask the child if there are enough cups to go in all the saucers. If he hesitates, ask him to find out. When there is one cup in each saucer remove the surplus, and place the six cups close together, leaving the saucers spread out. Ask him if there are still enough cups to go in all the saucers or if there are too many or too few. If he says there are enough cups, ask him why. A reply such as: "Of course, because I put one cup in each saucer," indicates that the child has grasped the concept of conservation (or invariance) of number.[†] If, however, he replies that there are not enough cups now, he is making a judgment on spatial grounds. This indicates that the child needs further matching experiences.

Number Relationships

You will readily understand that there is no point in trying to help children to learn their basic addition and subtraction facts until they understand the concept of conservation of number. They also need to discover the number relationships by firsthand experience using real objects in a variety of counting situations. For some children this experience needs to be repeated over and over again. They need to find out for themselves that it is not necessary to *count on* in ones to find that

the sum of 5 and 3 will always be 8. It can be an exciting discovery for young children that 5 + 3 and 3 + 5 have the same sum. This discovery halves the addition facts to be memorized. For every whole number trio (e.g. 3, 5, 8) there are four relationships eventually to be recalled:

$$5 + 3 = 8 \qquad 8 - 5 = 3$$
$$3 + 5 = 8 \qquad 8 - 3 = 5$$

When children meet subtraction for the first time, they usually solve this by addition. There are 8 boys and 5 girls in our group — how many more boys than girls? Some children would match boy-girl pairs and count the extra boys.

Structural Material

At this stage it is appropriate to consider the place of structural material, such as Cuisenaire, Stern, Color-Factor, Unifix, Dienes, etc., in the learning of arithmetic. When children first come to school they have already had considerable mathematical experience in their homes and in their immediate environment. An extension of this experience using real objects seems more natural and desirable than introducing *semi-abstract* coloured rods. Handling real objects is essential in these early stages. However, when a child is beginning to organize his number knowledge, structural material is not only very convenient, but provides another means of finding these number relationships. For example, he wants to build for himself all the number relationships whose sum is 8. The size, and in some cases, the colour of the structural material is a useful aid in helping the child arrange the material into meaningful patterns. Later, relationships concerning the four operations on numbers can also be developed by using structural material.

Some teachers prefer to create experiences to suit the needs of the children they teach. Many experiences have to be created because our number system is man-made. Some find structural material a valuable addition to the environmental experiences they provide for their students, particularly if introduced at the right time.

[†]This experiment is based on the works of Professor J. Piaget.
For further information about Professor J. Piaget see:
F. W. Land, *New Approaches to Mathematics Teaching* (London, MacMillan & Company, Limited, 1963).
or K. Lovell, *Growth of Mathematical Concepts* (London, University of London Press, Limited, 1961).

Mathematical Notation

Children see written numerals long before they understand their meaning: page 11, bus number 45, house number 284, etc. Gradually, through firsthand experiences, their number knowledge is extended. They can use numbers, record them and interpret many of the numerals they see day by day.

Some teachers introduce number symbols, or numerals, as part of their final counting activities. When the child knows and can write the digits he is then allowed to represent his counting in writing. He is encouraged to look for the patterns in our numeral system as he writes. Many children take a spirited interest in this activity and continue this *written counting* well into 4-digit numerals. As long as the interest is high, teachers should allow students to continue written counting because this practice is valuable.

After children have learned their numerals, when are they ready for notation or a mathematical way of recording experiences? The development is usually slow. Children need to experiment, talk and write in their own words long before they are ready for the introduction of symbols. If you wish, you may show your students the shorthand way or mathematical way of recording, but do not insist that they use this notation.

I shared 20 sweets among 4 children. They had 5 each.
$20 \div 4 = 5$

However, as soon as a child has a knowledge of numbers between 1 and 10, he should be encouraged to use symbols to record any basic number facts he knows: $1 + 5 = 6, 2 + 2 = 4, 1 + 2 = 3$, etc.

Again we wish to emphasize that symbolism and operational signs should not be introduced until children have had sufficient experience with materials to understand number concepts. Eventually children will adopt, or can be asked to adopt, the mathematical way of recording their experiences. At this stage they will begin to understand the relationship between addition and subtraction, division and multiplication. Once children can use notation it will help them to discover and to understand such properties as commutativity (i.e. $6 \times 4 = 4 \times 6$). This is an important discovery for them because the facts to be memorized are more than halved.

Basic Number Facts

There is only one way to find out whether a child knows basic number facts confidently without resorting to counting and that is by asking him orally. Written tests are of no use at this stage as there is no way of telling whether or not he is counting on (some children become very quick at this). At the same time it is possible to find out not only if he understands that he can add numbers in any order ($5 + 2$ or $2 + 5$), but if he uses this to his advantage.

The next stage is to extend this knowledge to numbers between 10 and 20. Commercial material can help children to discover the repetitive pattern of numbers from 1 to 10 and 11 to 20. This pattern is not obvious from the number names one-eleven or two-twelve; however, children seldom need be told the pattern for larger numbers since they can listen and discover these for themselves. Teachers need to devise oral activities to help children discover the pattern obtained when 10 is added to other numbers.

A number line, fastened horizontally to the wall, is invaluable at this stage. It can be 100" long and made from one-inch squared paper, 2" wide. Number strips, stiffened with hardboard or *stiff card,* 1" to 10" long and 1" wide, should be used with the number line. Number strips can be in red for emphasis. This will give children a visual method of discovering number patterns. Some teachers prefer to give each child a 20" desk number strip for use with the short strips, but the 100" strip is also essential. As with numbers less than 10, numbers between 10 and 20 should be tested orally. This testing is best done with small groups and sometimes with individuals.

A thorough understanding of adding 10 to other numbers will help children devise and develop a method for adding 9 to numbers:

$6 + 9 = 6 + 10 - 1 = 16 - 1 = 15.$
Adding 9 is difficult for many adults.

The extension of children's knowledge to include number relationships between 20 and 100 is a more lengthy process. Again, patterns such as $9 + 6 = 15$, $19 + 6 = 25$, $29 + 6 = 35$, etc. and those for $95 - 6 = 89$, $85 - 6 = 79$, etc. need to be discovered by each child for himself. Once these patterns are discovered and understood, you need to ensure that they are memorized. This requires a good deal of oral practice for some children (in small groups or individually). Once again, the only way to find out whether children know these number relationships is to ask individuals orally. The 100 square (which each child can make) or other structural material is useful at this stage. If children write the numerals for the 100 square alternately in black and red, they can use this for identifying odd and even numbers. A teacher of eight-year-olds had been discussing odd and even numbers with a group of nine children. She found that every child could say immediately whether or not any number up to 20 was odd or even. She asked each of them to paint a picture of his front door with the house number on it. When she asked them to collect the set of pictures with odd house numbers and the set with even house numbers she was met by blank expressions. Only Janet knew that her house number, 3, was odd; hers was the only number under 20.

Realizing that the children needed more experience the teacher then asked the group to make a *200 chart.* The children then wrote the numbers in order from left to right and top to bottom. The square included the highest house number, 177. When this was done they coloured the numbers alternately in black and red. Long before the chart was complete, the children were making discoveries such as: "All the numbers ending in 2 are in one column. They must be all even. So are all the 4's, the 6's, the 8's and the 10's." The teacher asked them why numbers ending in 7 came in the same column. The children soon realized the pattern results from repeated addition of 10.

Because of the colour coding, it was easy to decide whether a number was odd or even from the 200 chart. The children then produced two more diagrams of their own. (See p. 115.)

A one-hundred square

A two-hundred chart showing the house numbers of students

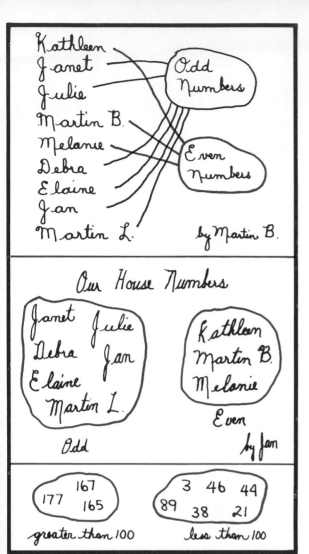

Using house numbers to introduce odd or even numbers

If the children had been one or two years older, the teacher might have asked them to sort out the odd numbers from the two sets invented by Jan and Martin, ({165, 167, 177} and {3, 21, 38, 44, 46, 89}).

A very common mistake made by teachers is the one made in the example above. We should not expect children to generalize or abstract after a limited experience. By providing the additional experience of the *200 chart* the teacher not only accomplished an understanding of odd and even numbers, but provided more experience for the following:

counting from 1 to 200
writing numerals from 1 to 200
patterns of 10
repetitive addition by tens

In addition, the teacher has provided each child with a chart that can be used for playing addition and subtraction games. These charts have additional benefits if they are constructed using numbers other than 10, such as those shown in figures 1 and 2 below. For example, the chart in fig. 1, constructed using the number 7, has the additional benefit of showing students the pattern of adding successive sevens to the other numbers. The chart in fig. 2, constructed using the number 6, can be used to find the prime numbers greater than seven. To do this you should mark out the columns containing numbers that have factors of 2 or 3. Next, mark out the diagonals containing numbers that have factors of 5 or 7. The remaining are prime numbers. This table can be continued up to 121.

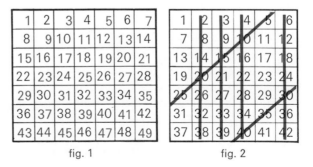

fig. 1   fig. 2

Number charts constructed with numbers other than 10

When are children ready to profit from written practice using tens and units? There is a simple test of readiness for this. Ask the child to add in his head two numbers such as 47 and 35. Ask him to describe how he did this. Suppose he said: "40 and 30, that's 70, and 7, 77." If, in order to add 5 he now counts "78, 79, 80, 81, 82," he is not yet ready for written practice. He requires further use of the number line and strips to establish the pattern 7 + 5, 17 + 5, etc. more firmly.

Place Value

One of the most difficult yet most important concepts related to counting is that of place value. The understanding of many of our procedures depends solely upon the student's comprehension of this concept. Of all the arithmetical concepts, the teaching of place value probably lends itself most readily to the use of manipulative materials. The first person to do extensive work in this area was Dr. Zoltan Dienes. Dr. Dienes conducted experiments with young children working in different bases using his *multibase* arithmetic blocks. He first introduced these blocks to seven-year-olds. There were sets in base 3, 4, 5, 6 and 10. Each base set consisted of units, longs, flats and blocks.

In base 3
3 units could be exchanged for 1 long
3 longs could be exchanged for 1 flat
3 flats could be exchanged for 1 block

Dr. Dienes's idea was that with varied experience of the difficult idea of place value, children would abstract the concept for themselves. Certainly young children, of ages 7 or 8, use the bricks with ease, moving from one base to another without confusion. A lengthy *play* period of several weeks is advisable; children should be allowed to build and play with the materials for a short time each day. From this play period they soon learn the equivalences of the various pieces. Subsequently, children can perform the four operations with the blocks, gradually doing this in a more systematic way, and recording their results in columns.

Children quickly discover that the largest number of pieces of the same kind in any column will be one less than the base number. In base 5, for example, the largest number will be 4 because they can always exchange 5 pieces for one of the next

blocks	flats	longs	units

A recording form for multibase blocks

blocks	flats	longs	units
(1)	(2)	(3)	(3)

Using drawings to record place value experiences

blocks	flats	longs	units
1	2	6	8
1	4	7	5
(sub-totals) 2	6	13	13
2	7	4	3

Recording, combining and separating activities

larger pieces. If a child has 5 unit blocks he can exchange these for 1 long; similarly, 5 longs can be exchanged for one flat, and 5 flats for one big block.

There are many activities that can be devised around place value blocks such as the Dienes blocks. A wide assortment of exchanging and counting activities are usually introduced first. These are followed by combining and separating activities. For example, in base 10, children might be given the following problem: combine 1 block, 2 flats, 6 longs, 8 units with 1 block, 4 flats, 7 longs, 5 units. It is important that children make the proper exchanges in order to get the final answer.

Since it is not necessary that children know how to write their numerals (they can draw pictures) these place value activities can be introduced at a very early stage. The goal of these preliminary activities is to work in base 10 so that the terminology: blocks, flats, longs, units, may be replaced with the more common terminology: thousands, hundreds, tens, units.

Place value blocks can also be useful in teaching some concepts in multiplication. Children can discover that multiplying by the base number results in a repetition of the original pattern with zero in the units place. In base 5, 2 flats, 3 longs, 4 units, multiplied by 5, becomes 2 blocks, 3 flats, 4 longs, 0 units. Children may invent their own names for the pieces of apparatus: cubes, squares, rods, units.

It is helpful to know that many other commercial materials of this nature can be purchased. Many teachers have also asked the shop or handicraft teachers in secondary schools to make place value blocks.

7-2. Addition, Subtraction, Multiplication and Division

Operations were formerly called *the four rules or processes.* Whether or not children are able to devise their own methods of written calculation for the operations will depend, to a great extent, on the firsthand experiences they are given. These experiences are particularly helpful if given in the initial stages. Experiences should be planned in all aspects of arithmetic: number, money, length, weight, capacity, time, etc.

How can we plan our work so that children will not only understand what they are doing but will also be able to devise their own methods of written calculation? A major aim should be to allow children the same opportunities to investigate in arithmetic (even in the field of computation) as in other aspects of mathematics. You can achieve this by:

1/ giving pupils varied and carefully planned experiences;

2/ introducing the language they need to describe these experiences, orally at first and then in writing;

3/ helping them to memorize, once understanding is reached, the basic number facts they require if they are to become efficient in calculations.

Computation

How will you know when children *are* ready for memorization of number facts? How will you know when children are ready to attempt written calculations? How will you know when children need practice in written calculations? How much practice do they require?

The answers to these questions depend on many variables, and there is no general answer for each specific situation. The following points may help you to determine when children are ready.

1/ They must have the necessary number knowledge we have already outlined.

2/ There is no point in asking children to write sums on paper when they can do the calculations in their heads — and recount their method.

3/ You will need to plan experiences which will require children to do certain calculations to solve a real problem. In the first instance they should be encouraged to devise and to carry out their own methods. These will probably be primitive, but by discussion within the group and as a result of questions from you, the methods will soon be refined.

4/ In general, flexibility of method should be encouraged. A group of 8 children may well produce 8 different methods which can be discussed and appraised. This is particularly desirable in the many problem situations which children will meet — and for which they will find a variety of solutions.

5/ Nevertheless, every child needs to have an efficient method for each of the four operations which he uses. To achieve this, he will require some practice at intervals, perhaps once a week at first; later once a month may suffice. Even practice can and should be fun. At the same time some oral work on *number and measure* relationships is necessary, sometimes with small groups, occasionally with an individual with special weaknesses, rarely, if ever, with a class. Overpractice is more harmful than too little practice as it leads to boredom. If children help in keeping records of their own progress they will help you to decide how much practice they need to attain and maintain efficiency.

Addition.   Children often require addition when checking materials or keeping records of class collections they are making. They find for themselves that vertical addition is more convenient than horizontal addition. This may be intuitive — or caught from others. If they are ready for this they will not use *props* for carrying figures. Results of a lengthy addition can be checked by using structural material or calculating machines.

Subtraction.   The natural methods are addition (complementary addition) and regrouping (decomposition). The latter presents no difficulty if children have had plenty of real practice, e.g. change from money, differences in length, weight, time and capacity. Real subtraction experience, with environmental or structural material always leads to solutions by addition or decomposition (regrouping). Often, when recording results, children will not record the original problem but the *converted* one

$$\begin{array}{r} 99 \quad 1 \\ \quad 2 \quad 7 \\ \hline 97 \quad 4 \end{array}$$

1001 would be written $\begin{array}{r} 1001 \\ -27 \end{array}$

or they may well *add* to 27 to obtain 1001. The word "borrow" is often incorrectly used. For example, when subtracting 47 from 83, it is not uncommon to find children reasoning: "I can't take 7 from 3. Borrow 1 from the 8 and make the 3 thirteen. Seven from thirteen is six and four from seven is three." In arithmetic we are changing or converting, not borrowing. In the example, 8 tens were converted to 7 tens and 10 ones. Results should always be checked by addition.

It is interesting to notice that older children and adults frequently invent an efficient method of *equal addition* without noticing that they have done so. Subtracting 38 from 105 is often calculated mentally by saying 40 from 107 is 67, in which 2 has been added to each number. This is a very mature idea, far too sophisticated to be introduced at the age of 8.

Multiplication.   Children are not ready to memorize multiplication facts until they know basic addition facts such as 5 + 7, 15 + 7, etc. Suppose a child knows 5 × 7 = 35 and needs 6 × 7; if he has to count on in ones: 36, 37, 38, 39, 40, 41, 42, instead of recalling and using 35 + 7 = 42, then he is not ready to memorize multiplication facts.

More practice with the number strips and other repetitive addition activities is needed before he is ready to continue. There are many ways in which you can help children to learn their multiplication facts (grouping in families: 2, 4; 5, 10; 3, 6; etc.). The number 9 has a special appeal to children once they have discovered that the sum of digits of the multiples of 9 is also 9:

9	18	27	36	
(9)	(1 + 8)	(2 + 7)	(3 + 6)	etc.

This pattern helps even a slow child to realize that 6 × 9 can never be 56!

There are some children with poor memories who make heavy weather of memorizing tables. Since it is important that they should not be given a distaste for mathematics, it is best to allow them to use a *ready reckoner table* when necessary. Games at this stage may help students over their difficulty. Competition among children at about the same stage is motivating if there is some degree of success for everyone.

An earlier example (page 13) stated how a group of 7-year-old children solved the problem of finding the number of pieces of macaroni in a pound bag by constantly refilling a container for which they counted the number of pieces required to fill it. They performed the resulting calculation, 6½ containers of 110 pieces, by first grouping in pairs and then by repeated addition. They were clearly ready to begin multiplication by single digits. They might have been asked to repeat the problem with another container (it is unlikely that the second total would have been as easy as 110), or their teacher might have said: "Suppose you had 4 containers with 123; how would you work this out? 7 containers?" etc. From a small group of children several methods would probably be suggested and the relative merits of these discussed. At this stage the children might be eager to do some practice, but real problems should be given at frequent intervals so that the children *know* why they are practicing multiplication.

When children first come across the need to do long multiplication they must be very familiar with multiplying by 10 first. See that they can count in tens when they count collections. Give them a large collection of acorns, pebbles or marbles to see how they organize this. When asked, for example, what the zero stands for in 170, they should reply: "It means there are no units."

In the example of p. 13, the cups contained 57 pieces of macaroni and there were 40 cups. The children (and 8-year-olds would find a way of solving this) might be asked to arrange the cups in groups which would help them to find the answer quickly. If they do not think of arranging the cups in tens they need some preliminary practice in counting collections, arranging these in tens, and in groups of 10. They should then be asked if this will help them to count the contents of the cups. This should help them to suggest:

10 cups hold   570
                570
                570
                570
             2280

A further question would encourage them to do this by multiplication

$$\begin{array}{r} 570 \\ \times\ \ \ \ 4 \\ \hline 2280 \end{array}$$

Finally, they should be given a problem for which they will need to multiply; for example, 47 × 65. Their own methods will be varied, but eventually they may arrive at:

47 (60 + 5) and work this in two parts
(Distributive Law)
60 times 47   or   47 × 60 = 2820
 5 times 47   or   47 × 5 =   235
65 times 47   or   47 × 65 = 3055

They can then be shown the more convenient way of writing this:

$$\begin{array}{r} 47 \times 65 \\ 65 \\ \hline 2820 \\ 235 \\ \hline 3055 \end{array}$$

Pupils will require some practice – but again, this should be interspersed with real problems which give rise to multiplication – and practice must not be given to the point of boredom. Finding squares of numbers is something which fascinates children, especially when they notice the pattern. Finding squares also gives them a great deal of incidental practice in multiplication as does the making a 20 by 20, or a 24 by 24 multiplication square.

Division.   First it is essential that children should have had ample experience with these aspects of division: sharing and subtraction. Many children, and their teachers, have been confused by the operation of division because they do not realize that there are two aspects. The first aspect of division a child meets is usually sharing. For example, a four-year-old can share a bag of candies among the four children in his family before he can count, by offering the bag to each in turn. Each child receives one at a time over and over again until the bag is empty. Contrast this with the question asked about another bag of candies. How many children can have 4 each? If the total is unknown each child in turn takes his share of 4 until the bag is empty. In the sharing aspect of division (sharing done one piece at a time) the information known is the number of children and we finish by knowing the share. In the subtraction aspect of division the information known is the share and we end by knowing the number of children. When a teacher first introduces $4\overline{)20}$ he usually says, "How many 4's in 20?" This is the subtraction aspect of division. If he has only given experience with the sharing aspect of division, pupils cannot associate this question with the experience. They also need experience with the subtraction aspect to prepare for division. $4\overline{)20}$ can also represent the sharing aspect but the questioning must be different. In order to share 20 among 4 children the teacher should ask, "How many will each of you get?" or "What is a quarter of 20?"

When the numbers become larger, children will need to devise a method for written calculations involving division, but as with multiplication, they first need to meet a *situation* which requires division.

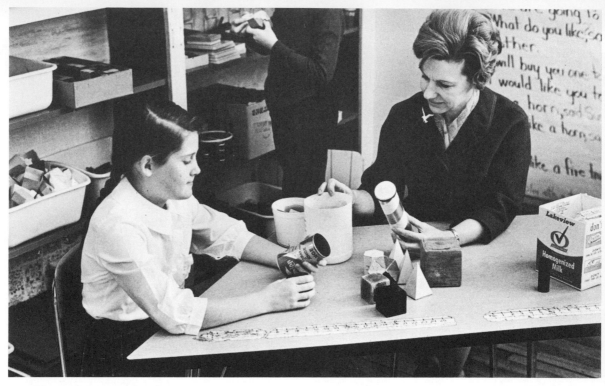

A teacher asked a group of 8-year-olds how many weeks there were in 50 days, 80 days, 110 days, etc. Answers came immediately until 110 days was reached; the children then demanded paper and pencil. Each child used a different method, from the boy who subtracted 1 week at a time to another who wrote:

```
110 days
 70 days      10 weeks
 40 days
 35 days       5 weeks
  5 days      15 weeks
```

The group discussed each method in turn and were so impressed by the convenience of the above method that all decided to adopt it.

The teacher tried them with 200 days. All but one wrote:

```
days
200
 70          10 weeks
130
 70          10 weeks
 60
 56           8 weeks
  4 days     28 weeks
```

The exception was the boy who first subtracted 70 days in the original example. He added a further refinement:

```
days
200
140          20 weeks
 60
 56           8 weeks
  4 days     28 weeks
```

and so saved one step.

Once more the group discussed the new method but at that time, it did not appeal to them. The teacher was interested to notice that one by one they began to refine their own methods. Gradually she introduced real problems which involved division by numbers greater than 10. The children had been asked to find the weight of a gallon of water. They tried several methods, including standing on bathroom scales holding a 2-gallon bucket, but their answers were so varied that a boy looked up the information in a book. He found, "A cubic foot of water weighs 1000 ounces. How many pounds is that?" he asked. He wrote:

ounces
1000
<u> 160</u>   10 lb
840
160   10 lb

At this point the teacher set the whole group on to the problem, encouraging them to look for an efficient method. She received:

ounces
1000
<u> 480</u>   30 lb
520
<u> 480</u>   30 lb
40
<u> 32</u>   <u> 2 lb</u>
8   62 lb

and another:

ounces
1000
<u> 960</u>   60 lb
40
<u> 32</u>   <u> 2 lb</u>
8   62 lb
62½ lb

The teacher decided that the children were ready for practice in division and that it was no longer necessary to give them a problem first, although every now and then she supplied the calculation to be done and asked the children to make a problem to fit this. This group of children had devised their own method of division and had been helped by the teacher to refine their method until it became efficient and understood by everyone. Since the method was their own, they did not require much practice to *fix the method.*

Fractions. Once a child understands the written notation of fractions, the only other concept he is required to learn is that of equivalence of fractions. As long as the calculations he is required to do are realistic, he will have no difficulty, even with division.

A boy cutting lengths of 1³/₄ inches from one-yard lengths of balsa wood for struts for his airplane, calculated of his own accord:

36" is 144 quarter inches,
1³/₄" is   7 quarter inches,

I shall get ¹⁴⁴/₇, or 20 pieces from each one-yard length.

A property of fractions which often puzzles children in the early stages is that although 24 is greater than 12, $1/24$ is less than $1/12$. Finding the thickness of different threads provides an experience which children never forget. Some nylon thread is so fine that it takes 72 strands wound on a card (or ruler) to make an inch, whereas a child may wind only 16 strands of coarse string to make an inch. Many similar experiences can be devised. *Mathematics in Primary Schools* [†] presents a detailed discussion of fractions.

When students learn algebra and have a thorough understanding of division as the inverse of multiplication and of subtraction as the inverse of addition, they should discover for themselves that division by a fraction is equivalent to multiplication by its inverse or reciprocal.

7-3. Length

One of the most natural experiences for active learning is that of measuring. A child's curiosity is easily stimulated by such questions as: Who is the tallest? Which is the largest?

There are many kinds of measurements: length, area, volume, time, and so on. We will not attempt to discuss all the different kinds of measurements that can be used for active learning at this time; we will, however, present the more common ones. Also, we would like to point out that the order in which these measurements are presented here is not necessarily the order in which you and your students may wish to study them. More specifically, your students may be interested in volume first if they are studying three-dimensional shapes.

The following aspects will need to be covered with each measurement: comparison, conservation, reiteration, standard units, precision and accuracy, and metric system. Here again the order listed is not necessarily the order in which they should be taught. Development will depend on the experiences given to children and the questions they ask. The junk box and bit (textiles) box will provide opportunities and material for measuring.

Vocabulary should be introduced gradually to match the varied experiences in the classroom. Some of the terms you will want your students to become familiar with are long (longer, longest),

†The Schools Council, *Mathematics in Primary Schools,* Curriculum Bulletin No. 1, 2d ed. (London, Her Majesty's Stationery Office, 1966), pp. 44-47.

and Related
Activities
for Primary
Grades*

121

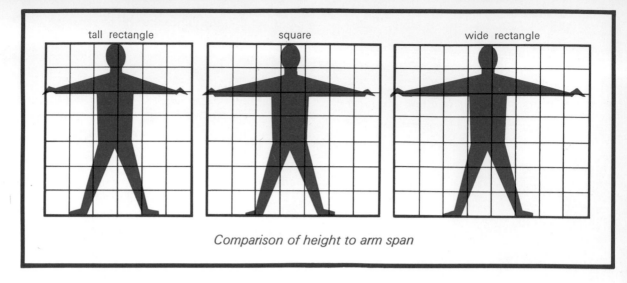

tall rectangle   square   wide rectangle

Comparison of height to arm span

short, tall, wide, narrow, thick, thin, flat, broad, round, perimeter, distance, straight, curved, diagonal, circumference, diameter, height, width, and the names of three-dimensional and two-dimensional shapes.

Comparisons

It is advisable to begin the comparison of length with just two measurements: two lengths or two heights, etc. If children have not had previous experience with comparisons, more than two measurements are usually confusing. Some questions that might be asked to introduce a unit on comparison of length follow.

Are you taller (or shorter) than your friend? How can you find out? (This will probably be done by direct comparison.)

Find one person taller and one shorter than you are. Is there anyone in the class of the same height as you are?

Find some things which are exactly the same length as the green stick. Is the room longer than it is wide? How can you find out? Are you a square? (i.e. are you as tall as you are wide – arms outstretched?) Find the set of squares, the set of tall rectangles and the set of wide rectangles in your class.

Allow the children to use any units they choose, even if these are not *equal* units; however, have plenty of equal units available: long sticks in one colour, short sticks in another colour, drinking straws, tongue depressors, long and short strips of ribbon or ticker tape. One teacher labelled the corners of her classroom: *Tall Things Here, Short Things Here*, etc.

If children are ready for notation you may wish to introduce the sign for *is greater than,* >, and the sign for *is less than,* <.

John's height > Bill's height

When children understand the concepts involved in comparing two lengths, then activities involving the comparison of more than two lengths; that is, size ordering, should be introduced. Material for this needs to be attractive and could be made by the teacher and the children: a set of 5 dolls, each a little taller than the preceding doll. These could be made of pipe cleaners and dressed all alike. Each doll should have a hat or a bag appropriate to its size in the sequence. A sequence of trees or three-bear sequence might also be used in size ordering. Present the material out of order to the child. Use 3 at first and gradually increase the number in the set. Ask him to rearrange the dolls in order, beginning with the smallest, and to give each one the hat (or bag) to fit it. Disarrange again, take out the second largest doll (for example) and ask the child to find its bag. Usually the child will require varied practice before he realizes that he has to arrange both (or all three) sets in order of size before he can do this unerringly.

Mapping can be used as an alternative way of representing relations as shown below.

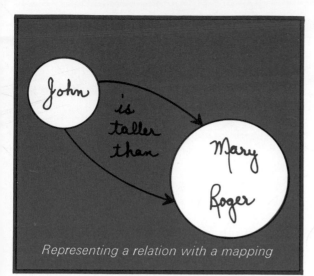

Representing a relation with a mapping

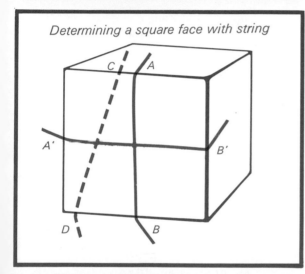

Determining a square face with string

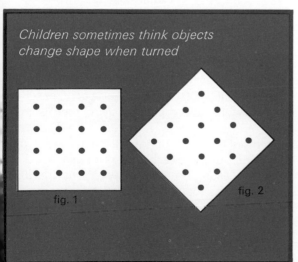

Children sometimes think objects change shape when turned

fig. 1   fig. 2

Conservation

Some 7- and 8-year-olds sorted all boxes (cuboids) with a square end into one set. They described their collection as tall squares, flat squares and square squares (cubes). They were asked how they knew the boxes they had chosen had square faces. (The teacher had hidden the rulers to encourage the children to think of other methods.) Peter took a piece of string and stretched it across the middle of one square end, first in position AB, then in position $A'B'$. The teacher asked him if the string in position CD would be the same length as AB. He hesitated, said that the teacher's string was not "straight" and finally moved his own string to the edge, matched the length, cut it off and then compared this with the adjacent edge. Not one child in the group began by comparing adjacent edges, although each was concentrating on his own box. Later a girl drew around the "square" end of the box and rotated the box to see if it fitted in the second position.

Except for the girl, the children in the previous example may well have had difficulty because of their lack of understanding of the concept of conservation of length; that is, that the length of an object remains the same in whatever position the object is placed. Even nine-year-olds, if they lack experience of actual measuring, may not grasp this concept. A young teacher giving a small group of children their first experience in making shapes with elastic bands on a square geo-board found that they could not continue when the board was moved from the position shown in figure 1 to that shown in figure 2. As they discussed this it became clear that the children thought the board had changed its shape. They insisted that the marked angles were now larger than before and that all the sides had become longer. It was some time before the children were able to convince themselves that the boards were still exactly the same size and shape in the new position. They were making judgments on spatial grounds because they lacked measuring experience.

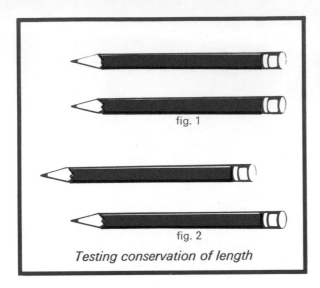

fig. 1

fig. 2

Testing conservation of length

Surprisingly, this concept is sometimes acquired after conservation of volume and area. Piaget questions whether children should be given measuring experience before they understand that an object remains the same length no matter in what position it is placed. On the other hand, many believe that children acquire this concept as a result of measuring experience. Experiments to find whether or not children have acquired this concept are easy to devise. For example, use two pencils which a child has matched and declared to be of the same length, fig. 1. When one pencil is moved into a different position, fig. 2, ask the child whether or not the pencils are still of the same length.

It is also important to test his reaction to the lengths of edges of cubes and squares in different positions and to a framework made of four equal strips in a variety of configurations.

Reiteration of the Unit

Some eight-year-olds were asked to measure the width of the room. "It's six and a half bodies," they replied. "Whose body?" they were asked. Three friends stood up. Paul and Blair were of the same height, but Roger was at least a head taller than the other two. (They had laid themselves head-to-foot across the room.) The teacher asked them if there would be any difference if they had used Roger only. "Yes," was the reply, "Roger would be very tired." The teacher pressed them further: "But would you get six and a half 'Rogers'?" she asked. All but one insisted that the answer would

still be 6½ bodies because they were measuring the same distance. Ann, however, said that there would be fewer "Rogers" because he was taller than his friends. Here was a good starting point for the need first for an equal unit and then for standard units.

Many teachers achieve the concept of reiteration by asking each child in a group to measure the width of a room in his own foot lengths. This involves repeating or reiterating the unit. The 8-year-olds who measured the width of the room in "bodies" were repeating their units. They were ready to be asked to measure the distance first in "Pauls" and then in "Rogers." They used the line of square tiles to keep straight. If there had been no guidelines, the children would have had greater difficulty.

You need to *starve* them of regular units of measure. When children cannot find sufficient units they usually decide for themselves to repeat their unit over and over again. Ask them first to estimate the number of units they will need to cover a long distance such as the length of a corridor or yard and then to check their answer. It is important to ask children to *estimate* first because this makes them more interested in the answer. "How near were you? Who was nearest?" Such questions are sometimes difficult for young children to answer.

Standard Units

In the preceding example are questions that might be discussed: Which is the better measure, 6½ bodies or 6½ Pauls? Would 6½ Pauls mean anything to children of another school? If we were going to write a letter to students in another school, to tell them how wide our school room is, would 6½ bodies have any meaning? Would 6½ Pauls have any meaning? How could we measure our school room so that the students in another school would be able to compare the size of their room with ours?

In discussing questions similar to these, children are usually quick to see the need for a standard unit of measure. There are many projects that may be introduced that allow children to investigate which units are standard and how these standards are kept.

Once standard units are discussed, determined, and the relationships between them understood, children can use them to make measurements that are of interest to them, such as height and waist. One class of ten-year-olds in England became very interested in the height-waist ratio of people. In fact, one student invented the term "index of rotundity." They noted that this index was remarkably constant. They not only found the index of rotundity of all the people in their own school and village, but also of the people in the next village. They wanted to know whether anyone would have an index of 3. This involved a great deal of measuring, as well as a lot of practice in division!

Precision and Accuracy

Ask the children to find some things about the same length as their foot rule or yardstick (also some things longer and some things shorter). This usually causes them to look more closely at the bits left over — and to use a second unit.

The degree of precision, hence the unit selected, depends upon the accuracy desired. Activities should be provided to help children discover that it is just as unsuitable to use a small unit to measure a long distance as it is to use a large unit to measure a very short distance. For example, measuring the length of a room with an inch unit would not only be a most difficult task, but, for normal purposes, would be an inappropriate choice of unit because it is too precise. On the other hand, measuring the length of a pencil with a yard unit would also present a problem in precision.

Children often find yards easier than feet to start with — but when they have become familiar with both units, and later with inches, and have discovered for themselves the relationship between these units, they should be allowed to choose the units they consider more convenient and appropriate.

All measurements are approximations. There is no such thing as an "exact measurement." Every time we measure a length we have to make a decision about the degree of precision appropriate to the situation or problem in hand. This done, we must then decide which measuring instrument is most suitable. If we take a yardstick to measure 100 yards the marked distance could easily be 1 yard out, or off, because each chalk mark could be ⅛ inch thick.

In measuring index of rotundity the children discussed the degree of precision and accuracy which would be sensible for measuring waists and heights. They eventually decided that when they were wearing clothes, measurement to the nearest inch would be more sensible than to the nearest half-inch. They made a similar decision about measuring heights and commented: "It makes the division easier, too." They also had to decide on the degree of accuracy required for the index. "It's no use giving it as a whole number," a girl said, "we shall all have the same index of 2." Fractions were difficult to compare, so they decided to give the index to one decimal place.

The question of accuracy often arises when children are measuring very thin things. A group of ten-year-old boys decided to find the thickness of every piece of paper and cardboard in the storage cupboard. At first they measured out 1 inch of paper and counted the number of sheets. But when they came to the thin paper, counting became boring and some decided to measure ¼ inch of it instead. Others counted ½ inch "to check accuracy." The difference in their results for the thin paper made the boys decide to give their answer to the nearest 10 sheets (390 sheets to an inch). Still others counted 100 sheets of paper, measured the thickness (0.3") and obtained the thickness of a sheet as .003". This led to further discussion about which was the best or most reliable answer, and how the two answers $1/390$" and .003" could be compared. Finally the teacher suggested that they should check the thickness with a micrometer, if they could find out how to use this instrument. (Boys are usually quicker at this than girls.) After they had learned to use the micrometer they also compared the thickness of this thin paper with the thickness of human hair.

Making a life-size model of Goliath can present a challenging problem in precision to children of various ages. How broad would his shoulders be? Would he be a "square"? How long would his sword be? What size shoes would he take? These are questions which intrigue ten-year-olds. The range of investigation will depend on the materials available and the extent to which the children's imagination can be aroused.

Making a graph showing shoe sizes

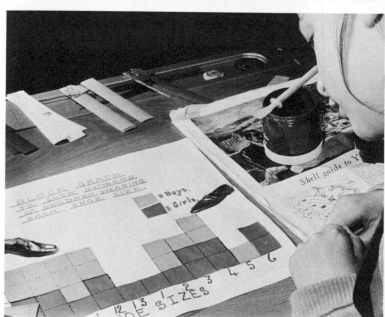

Metric System

In these days of international scientific influence pupils ought also to have experience with metric units of length. They can first find their vital statistics, see Chapter 6 page 80, in metric units, centimetres and metres for length and kilograms for weights. They can discover for themselves by practical experiment or from reference books such approximate equivalences as the number of centimetres in a foot (and in an inch), the number of metres in 100 yards (cotton reels give this), the number of yards in 100 metres, and the number of kilometres in 5 miles. Some cars have both miles and kilometres on the odometers or milometers so comparisons are straightforward.

It is a good idea to have a *metric month* during which the children do all their measuring in metric units so that they become thoroughly at home with these. This is a good plan for teachers, too!

7-4. Perimeter and Area

Because perimeter and area of regular shapes, such as rectangle and square, usually involve the same variables, pupils often confuse perimeter and area. We therefore suggest you choose irregular shapes to introduce area and perimeter concepts. Questions such as

Who in the class, has the smallest footprint?
Who has the smallest waist?
Can you find a ball or box that has the same perimeter as your waist?

motivate the interest of students in this topic.

Children, aged 7 and 8, when comparing their footprints decided to choose the longest and shortest in the class. As they were doing this they noticed that the longest was not necessarily the widest. After much discussion they decided the only way they could compare their footprints was to find out how much surface each covered. To determine this each of the children drew an outline of one of his feet. Some used fabric with a pattern of squares or other congruent shapes on it; others used 1-inch squared paper to find which footprint covered the most surface. Those who used squared paper found it a help to number the whole squares.

Part squares were dealt with in various ways: neglected; estimated as ¼, ½ or ¾ squares; large parts were paired with small parts; large parts were counted as whole squares and small parts neglected. Some children exchanged *feet* to check each other's method. This activity was culminated by making a graph which showed the various shoe sizes in the class.

A group of 9-year-old children found the areas of their feet in order to find the pressure on each square inch of foot when standing on both feet. A girl found the pressure on each square inch of her feet to be about 2½ lbs. She then decided to find the comparable information for an elephant. She made a tracing of an elephant's foot in a museum. Allowing for the fact that the elephant has *four* feet, she was surprised to find that the average pressure on each square inch of an elephant's feet was only 10 lbs! This work led to discussion as to whether or not weight was evenly distributed.

Conservation of Area

Seven- and eight-year-olds enjoy making tangrams; that is, cutting 6-inch coloured squares to make pictures. All of each square must be used to make a complete picture. Children are then asked whether or not they have the same amount of coloured paper as they had at the outset.

Another way of testing the concept of conservation of area is to ask children to paint the outside of a box. Ask them to flatten the box, then ask if it would have taken more or less paint to paint it flattened out.

Measuring Round Things
(Circumference/Diameter Relationships)

In order to facilitate the measuring of round things we suggest you make a collection of objects of various sizes such as cylindrical tins and bottles, balls, plates, filter papers, wheels and circular discs of hard board. Ask pupils to guess the diameter and the circumference[†] of each object. They can then be encouraged to check these guesses. It is helpful to have inch strips of various lengths (with one-inch graph paper) so that children can measure round things, including themselves. Most children like to make an illustrated book about themselves.

Some 6-year-olds were asked by their teacher if they could *measure* a collection of balls. They used a different colour of string for each ball and found its circumference by stretching the string around the widest part. They then arranged these lengths of string in order to make a *natural* graph and recorded the lengths to the nearest half-inch. To the teacher's disappointment, they made no further comment and lost interest in the topic.

Some 8-year-olds tried to measure the diameters of a collection of tin lids. They found this difficult so they traced around each lid on paper. After some unsuccessful attempts to draw a line through the centre, they decided to cut the paper circle out and to fold it in half. They guessed that half the circumference would be twice this diameter and were much surprised to find that the paper collars they made to fit each lid were about three times the corresponding diameters.

A group of 10-year-olds tackled the same problem in a different way. They found it difficult to measure the saucepan lids, tins, bottles and trundle wheel they had collected, and so they decided to use *direct* measurements to make a graph. They marked the diameters along the horizontal axis, made a collar in narrow (coloured) cellulose tape for each object and placed this at the end of the corresponding diameter, thus making a column graph. A boy noticed that the tops of the columns seemed to be in a straight line so he stretched a long piece of string through the tops. This passed through zero. After some thought the boy explained this: "If there's no circle, there'll be no diameter or circumference." This graph proved very useful.

Measuring the diameters of balls presents a more challenging problem and should be reserved for older children. Finding the diameter/circumference relationship of a set of balls is particularly difficult. Teachers, too, find this problem difficult. It is sometimes, but not always, easier to find the ratio of the circumferences of two balls than the ratio of their diameters. Does this give the same result? Unless calipers are available, it is often easier to measure the circumference of a round object than its diameter. All diameters can be read from a graph once the circumference is known.

†When discussing balls and other spherical objects we are interpreting circumference to be the circumference of a great circle.

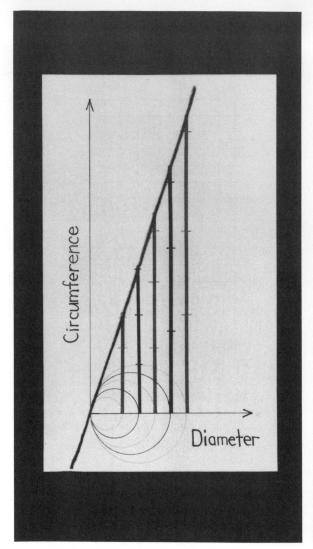

*Graph showing relation of area
to length of side*

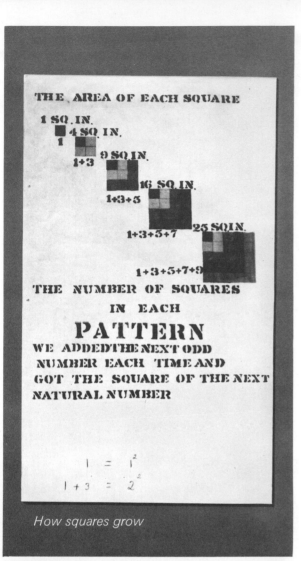

How squares grow

"In how many ways can you measure a square?" a teacher of nine- and ten-year-olds asked her class. The children made a set of squares from coloured unit squares of sides 1 unit, 2 units, 3 units, 4 units, etc. From this they obtained the following patterns:

Side	1	2	3	4	5	6
Perimeter	4	8	12	16	20	24
Area	1	4	9	16	25	36

After some discussion, a column for zero values was added to the table. "What will the perimeter graph look like?" the teacher asked. "A straight line because it goes up in 4's," Jane replied. The teacher disagreed until Jane explained that if she could include squares of 1½", 2¼" sides, she could fill in the spaces between successive points. Richard found successive differences between the areas to be 1, 3, 5, 7 ... — the odd number pattern. They decided that the graph of the areas could not be a straight line because the differences were not equal. "But it cannot be an uneven graph because there is a pattern," Jane said, "so it must be a curve." Their first curved graph is shown below.

The same ten-year-olds decided to investigate the area/diameter relationship of circles. They drew around their collection of tin lids on ¼" squared paper and counted the number of squares. They could not detect a pattern, so they drew a graph, making the diameter along the horizontal axis and the corresponding number of squares in the area along the vertical axis. Once more they included zero values and obtained a curve which resembled the *growth of squares* curve. They used this graph to find the diameters of circles of various areas, including 1 square foot.

This group was subsequently given a set of hardboard discs of the same thickness and of diameters 6", 9", 12" to 2 ft. After drawing the area/diameter graph for this set, they decided to weigh each disc. When they drew the weight/diameter graph they found that this closely resembled the area/diameter graph. During the

129

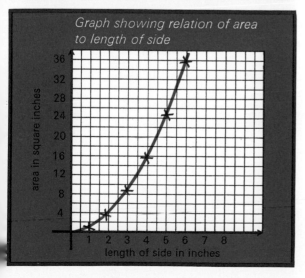

Graph showing relation of area to length of side

discussion which followed, the children established the reason for this. They then weighed a square foot of hardboard of the same thickness and used their graph to find the diameter of a circle of area 1 square foot. This agreed closely with the first value they obtained.

A group of eleven-year-olds who had found the area/side relationship of squares and the area/diameter relationship of circles next turned their attention to ellipses. (A boy had read from a book that an ellipse could be drawn by using a loop of string and two drawing pins.) They expected the circumference/diameter and area/diameter graphs to resemble the corresponding graphs for a set of circles and were disappointed to discover that the graphs for the set of ellipses were different. After much discussion they realized that the ellipse has an extra variable because its *diameters* are different.

Tessellations or Tiling

A group of 8-, 9- and 10-year-olds in a village school in Britain were studying bees. They wondered why the bee made hexagonal cells. To determine this children found ways of constructing regular shapes for themselves: triangles, squares, pentagons, hexagons and octagons. They experimented to find out which single shapes, repeated over and over again, would fit together. The hexagon was among these. They then set about to find why some regular shapes would *tile* while others would not. Finally their interest spread to irregular shapes. A ten-year-old wrote: "We were surprised to find that quadrilaterals would fit together. We knew that regular shapes, like squares, would fit together but the quadrilaterals looked so irregular." They did not finally satisfy themselves about the reason for the hexagonal cell of the bee until they began to experiment with a loop of paper of fixed perimeter and found the shape which would contain maximum area. Of the polygons that can be used for making tile patterns, the hexagon is nearest in shape to the circle.

There are many interesting activities that can be devised using constant perimeters or constant areas. Questions such as "What are the dimensions of the rectangle having the largest area with a perimeter of 16 inches? What are the dimensions of the rectangle having the largest perimeter with an area of 36 square inches?" are typical of those

A beehive is a good example of tessellation

Tessellating with rectangles

that may be asked to stimulate thought on this topic. The teacher should establish an interval for the second question; for example, find the dimensions to the nearest inch. If the students have worked with fractions they should be encouraged to experiment with fractional dimensions, particularly those less than one.

Both questions can be extended to three dimensions by using unit cubes. You will find the problems easier if you consider rectangular shapes before extending the problem still further.

Area, volume and perimeter problems arise in packaging goods of all kinds. What is the most economical shape of container considering economy of material only? Why are so many containers cylindrical in shape? For economy? For strength? For ease of manufacture?

7-5. Volume and Capacity

For convenience of reference, volume and capacity, and area and perimeter have been treated as separate topics. In the classroom these subjects would often be interrelated.

Comparison

Water play gives valuable initial experience of filling containers to make comparisons of capacities. When does a young child first realize what we mean by a beaker full (to the brim)? Which holds more, the medicine bottle or the milk container? This question is not difficult for a 6-year-old who has had constructive water play experience. Invariably he fills the one he thinks is the larger and pours it carefully through a funnel for the pleasure of seeing the other container overflow. (See the film *Maths Alive*.) Compare this with a class of 12-year-old girls who were working examples of the traditional type on rectangular volumes. They were asked to estimate which of two vases held more. There was some difference of opinion so they were asked to find out. The teacher pointed out that there was a sink in the room, but there was no response. Finally a girl said, "How can we do this without jam jars?" "What do you want the jam jars for?" she was asked. "To fill each vase and pour the water into jam jars and compare the levels" was the reply! This example illustrates the

added difficulties encountered when a teacher attempts to use an active learning approach on older students who have spent most of their school time working meaningless problems.

Conservation of Volume

Conservation of volume is implicit in much of a child's experience with water, but unless his teacher questions him about this, it may be some time before the concept becomes explicit and operational. A 5-year-old will pour water from a tall glass into a shallow dish and judge that there is less water in the dish because he is comparing one dimension, height. Long before he is 7 the same child may be saying emphatically: "Of course they are the same. I poured it from one to the other." He is now able to reverse the process in his imagination.

A problem which really tests whether a child understands this concept is to give him a large cylindrical jar containing water and two identical jars of smaller diameter and to ask him to halve the water in the large jar. He may be tempted, in this instance, to match levels in the large jar and one smaller jar.

Reiteration of the Unit

Some six-year-olds made a collection of small rectangular boxes. "Which contains most?" asked the teacher. Much discussion and some interesting writing followed this question as the children tried to clarify their ideas. They filled the boxes with sand and weighed each (box and all). This helped them to put the boxes in order but the sand ran out at the corners – so they looked for something else to fill the boxes. They tried and rejected beads and cubes of all sizes until a girl found a bead, shaped like a cube, which would fit into all the boxes. The cubes which filled each box were then placed above each box as shown and the work was set out on a table with the children's own writing.

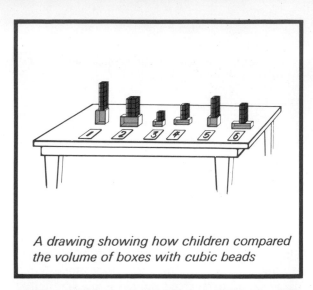

*A drawing showing how children compared
the volume of boxes with cubic beads*

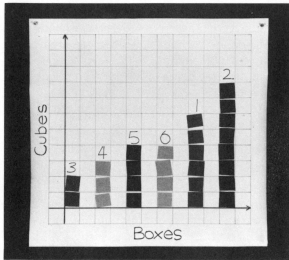

However, in the overcrowded classroom the
cubes were soon knocked off the table. This gave
a boy an idea. He made a graph on ½" square
paper (the bead was almost a half-inch cube)
and, starting this time from a common baseline,
he matched each cube with a square and made his
first block graph. "Can you see that boxes 5 and 6
hold the same number of cubes?" he wrote. "But
they are very different shapes of box," (showing
that he also understood conservation).

Standard Units

Finding containers that are clearly marked
in standard units is difficult. There are few
satisfactory measuring jugs. Many are marked in
diverse and confusing units such as pounds-
ounces, fluid ounces, quarts-pints and pints-
ounces. Moreover, jugs and pails have sloping
sides. Cylindrical containers in near-clear plastic
are probably the most convenient containers
for measuring volume, and these can be graduated
or calibrated by the children themselves. They may
choose cubic inches (a wooden cube has to be
held under water!) or cubic centimetres for a
small jar. A straight strip of graph paper fixed
vertically to the jar serves admirably. This, however,
may cause children to forget that they are
measuring volume.

Following are some important questions about
volume which can be answered by students
without help from the teacher:

*Find the volumes of sets of cylinders (a) on con-
gruent bases but with different heights (tall plastic
containers can be cut to different heights);
(b) of equal heights but different diameters.
Graphs for (a) and (b) can be compared and
discussed.
Find the volume of a ball (sphere) and that of a
cylinder which just contains the sphere. Later
this can be compared with the theoretical results.
Find the volume of a cone and that of a cylinder
which just contains the cone.
Find the number of marbles which occupy the
same volume as a ball.*

Volume by Displacement

To find the volume of irregular shapes students
need to know how to find the volume of an
object by water displacement. A useful activity
is to have students measure the amount water
rises when an object is placed in it. A *measuring
cylinder* can be calibrated by successively placing
one-inch cubes in the water and marking the
amount the water rises on a tape or strip of paper
mounted on the cylinder. The idea of displacement
is also needed for answering questions such as,
"How many times as heavy as water is the stone?"

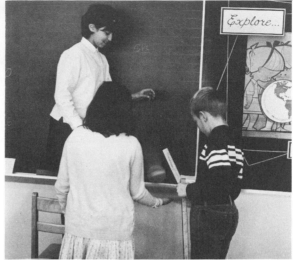

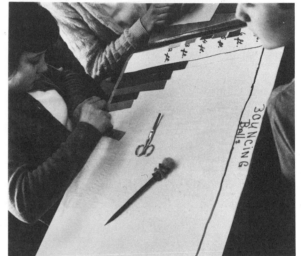

Using both cubes and sand to determine the capacity of a container

Material needed to compare the volumes of cylinders, cones and spheres

Measuring how high a ball bounces

Graphing the bounce of a ball

A large class of 10-, 11- and 12-year-olds were organized into five groups. Each group responded in different ways to the question: "In how many ways can you measure a ball?" The following suggestions were made:

See how high it bounces.
See how far it rolls when you start it at the top of a slope.
Weigh it. Find its circumference. Find its volume. Find its diameter.

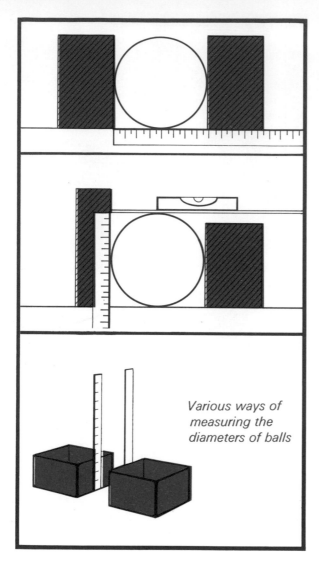

*Various ways of
measuring the
diameters of balls*

This last was done in two ways:

a/   By enclosing the ball between two blocks of wood and measuring the diameter with a ruler. Children were quick to see the advantages of starting from a whole number of inches on the ruler.

b/   By finding the height of the ball. Two blocks of wood were placed upright on the table with the ball in between. A ruler was put on top of the ball and a spirit level was used to ensure that the ruler was horizontal. The height of the ball was then read using a ruler.

Two boys made a vertical height scale by using two strips of 1/10″ graph paper pasted to two narrow strips of wood which were fastened to two small boxes.

The pupils next found the volume by displacement of water in a pail. They marked the water level before and after immersing the ball (which was held under the surface of the water by using a knitting needle). There was a good deal of discussion before the pupils finally decided to measure the volume of water between the two marks in the pail in fluid ounces. (They first had to discover what a fluid ounce was!) A variety of balls, some of solid rubber, and some filled with air, were investigated in this way. Graphs were drawn to see if there were relationships between pairs of variables.

7-6. Time and Speed

A knowledge of the history of man's struggles to measure time will give you some idea of the abstract nature of time and of the difficulties encountered in recording time. Children today have many experiences which concern time. They see clocks in many places: an electric clock with a revolving second hand, a clock on the electric cooker, a clock on the television screen, a pinger or timer clock in the kitchen, a 24-hour clock at the airport or railway station, and a clock in the automobile. They see television "timetables" and timetables for aircraft. There are calendars on the walls of their classrooms and homes. But these experiences may be meaningless unless their attention is directed to them.

A full understanding of "time in our lives" comes gradually with the knowledge that the earth rotates about its axis in 24 hours, and that the earth revolves about the sun in about 365¼ days. These movements of the earth cause, among other things, night and day and the four seasons which are all used to measure time. Man has arbitrarily divided the earth into 24 belts or zones to facilitate his keeping of time. The concepts of time are very difficult for young children. Because of this, we believe models of the earth and sun are essential for the teaching of time.

A number of activities to help children understand time are listed below.

Pictorial illustrations of the day's activities – can be made by the children: getting up, washing, breakfast, coming to school, etc.

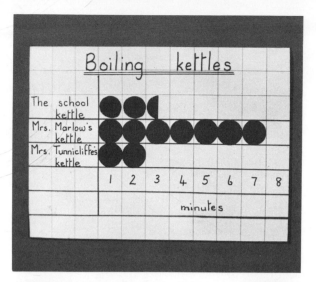

a girl wrote. All the children wrote about the
kettles and helped to make a pictorial representation on squared paper.

Various children wrote:

Mrs. T's kettle boiled the fastest of all the kettles.

Mrs. M's kettle took the longest to boil.

Mrs. M's kettle took 5 minutes more than
Mrs. T's kettle.

Mrs. M's kettle took 4½ minutes more than
the school kettle, because the school kettle
took 2½ minutes.

Mrs. T's is quicker than the school kettle.

Mrs. M's kettle boils slower than the school kettle.

Mrs. T's kettle boils ½ minute quicker than the
school kettle.

The school kettle took ½ minute longer than
Mrs. T's kettle.

This shows the wide variety of comments which
can arise from one piece of work.

Bedtime and getting-up-time provide
interesting activities for studying time. List the set
of children who get up at 7 A.M., 7:30 A.M., etc.
List the set of children who go to bed at 7 P.M.,
8 P.M., 9 P.M., etc. How many hours before
midnight? A more difficult question is *How many
hours were you in bed?*

A group of seven-year-olds decided that they
would make a chart about their bedtimes. The
teacher printed some clock faces reading 7
o'clock, 8 o'clock, etc. The children suggested
that they should each draw a picture of themselves
in bed. The teacher gave each child a piece
of paper of the same size for this and the children
pasted them on the chart in the appropriate time
set. Then they decided they would make another
illustrated chart of getting-up-times. The teacher
next asked them which children were in bed
longest. Without hesitation they replied: "The set
of children who go to bed at 7." The teacher
pointed out that Anita, who went to bed at
7 o'clock, got up before anyone else, at 6 o'clock.
"But it doesn't matter when you get up," was
the reply.

In her effort to help the children understand,
the teacher first helped each child to work out
how long he was in bed. They could not do this

Recognition of certain times – schooltime,
playtime, meal time, going-home-time, bedtime,
television programs, etc., first in hours then in
half-hour intervals, provide many interesting
classroom activities.

Children can watch the second hand of a clock
make one turn, the sand in an eggtimer run out,
or a plastic bottle empty. They can find what
they can do in one minute: thread 17 beads,
run round the yard, hop across the yard, or read
one page of a book. They can time mechanical
toys or toys running down a slope.

Some 7-year-olds decided to find the time
it took for 3 kettles to boil. "There were two pints
of water in each kettle. Two pints = 1 quart,"

The Number of Hours We Sleep

Keith	
Peter	
Cheryl	
Sylvia	
Jimmy	
Roger	
Susan	

1 2 3 4 5 6 7 8 9 10 11 12
Hours

for themselves at this stage. She drew a graph to help them (the beginning is shown in the figure), using a scale of 1 inch to represent 1 hour. "Now," she said, "can you tell me which of you is in bed the longest?" The children looked puzzled and said, "Oh no we can't, you've made us all go to bed at the same time." Wisely, the teacher abandoned her attempt for the time being. She, not the children, had introduced two ideas which made the problem too difficult for the children at this stage. The two ideas were the representation of a unit of time by a unit of length (1 inch represents 1 hour), and a common base line in order to compare lengths.

Telling the time

Telling the time is far easier when the child has his own watch. Use a watch or clock with second hand to time a minute, later a half-minute. How far can your friend walk in one minute? How much water can you collect from that tap in one minute? Can you put everything away in one minute?

Measuring Time—Making Time Machines

Children can make simple time machines: a sand clock, a water clock, a candle clock (teacher supervision), or a shadow clock. Children need to sit outside and watch the movement of the shadow before they can make careful measurements. Very young children think the stick, and not the shadow, moves. A very fascinating time machine is the pendulum. Even young children

are sometimes able to count the slow beats of a long pendulum to help them to measure an interval of time in pendulum beats.

A group of 8 boys of ages 9 to 11 selected various objects (toy trucks, balls and cylindrical objects) to roll down a long smooth slope in the corridor. For a minute or two, there was pandemonium as each boy rolled or pushed the object down the slope (and himself after it). When they had done enough exploring on their own, they were asked if they could find out how long each object took to run down the slope. "We need a stop-watch," said George. There was no stop-watch, so their teacher suggested that the boys might invent a timing device using the washers, plasticene and string he had provided. "We could make a pendulum," said Rickey. Bob noticed a hook attached to the ceiling above his head and the pendulum was soon swinging from it. "Does it beat regularly?" the teacher asked. "Let's count," said the boys. "Where shall we start?" was the next question. "Up at the ceiling and straight out," replied Earl. But no one could reach so another starting point was fixed. "Does it matter where we start?" asked the teacher. The boys were sure that it did matter, so this question was noted by the teacher for subsequent investigation.

The group chose a starter, judge and "counter" and the observations began. It was difficult to ensure that the ball rolled from rest and was not given a push. The string was long and the pendulum swung rather slowly. "Is there anything we can do to change the beat?" the teacher asked. "Shorten the string," suggested Rickey. "Add more plasticene," said Earl. The group experimented with the length until satisfied with the beat. "How shall we count?" asked the teacher. "The number of swings in half a minute," said Mervyn. Rickey used a watch with a "second" hand and a count was made using different lengths of string. (At first, Rickey had to start with the second hand at 12, but he was soon confident enough to start with the hand in any position.) "It swings much faster when we shorten the string," was the conclusion.

The boys had less success when the weight was altered because the point of suspension chosen was not rigid. The pendulum came to rest within two minutes of starting. After some discussion with the teacher, it was decided that a better point of suspension must be found and the experiments repeated in a more systematic way. Results could then be recorded in tabular and graphical form, as well as in words.

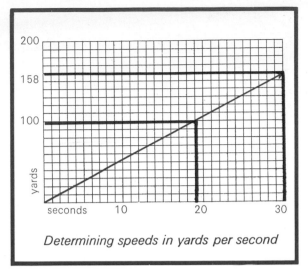

Determining speeds in yards per second

Calendar, Television Programs, Timetables

We do not make enough use of the large calendars in our classrooms for the discovery of number patterns.† A calendar is very useful for counting in sevens. "What do you think about the dates of all the Mondays this month?" is an example of questions about calendars.

Every time we find how long the television program lasts we are subtracting one time from another. Pupils should be encouraged to make up interesting problems for their peers. When the two times are on either side of noon, the 24-hour clock is a great aid. Time charts in history will help students to put events in chronological order.

Speed

"How long does my tortoise take to walk a yard?" is an example of a first question in quantitative speed a 7-year-old might ask. Such a question should be followed by extensive experience planned to develop the meaning of fast, slow, quickly. Timing is the first and easiest method for calculating a speed. It is the method frequently used by athletes. "How long does it take to run a mile? ¼ mile? 100 metres?"

At this stage pupils often want to express speeds in more familiar terms, such as miles per hour. Unless a graph is used, expressing speeds in these terms would involve difficult calculations. Above is an example of how a graph can be used to determine speeds in yards per second. A boy found that he could run 100 yards in 19 seconds. The teacher asked, "If you could run at the same speed, how far will you run in one minute? 1 hour?"

At this point other pupils joined in the experiment and suggested a graph would help. They decided that the point (0,0) should be included in

the graph since zero distance is run in zero time. After much discussion they decided the graph would be a straight line for a constant speed. The teacher then asked the children to determine from the graph how far they would run in 30 seconds, 20 seconds, 10 seconds and finally 1 second. They found that Jimmy could run a little more than 5 yards in a second. Then the children became interested in finding their own walking speeds and comparing their results.

Whenever speed is to be determined, a length has to be measured. Few adults have calculated their own walking speed by direct observation. This is a basic topic which presents unusual difficulty if firsthand experience has not been given, and yet young children will solve this problem in their own way if given the opportunity.

A class of nine-year-olds collected (and later released) insects and found the time each insect took to cover a foot. Some insects could not be persuaded to run in a straight line so foot lengths of string were cut to follow the path of the wayward insects. Their results, which were very attractively presented, ranged from five seconds for the ant to seven minutes for the snail. Gail, who was interested in caterpillars because her brother collected them, wrote the following of her own accord:

†Association of Teachers of Mathematics, *Notes on Mathematics in Primary Schools* (London, Cambridge University Press, 1967).

Determining time it takes an insect to travel one foot

To go one foot the caterpillar takes 45 seconds.
To go one yard the caterpillar takes 3 × 45 seconds
or 135 seconds.
She calculated that at this rate the caterpillar would
cover one mile in 66 hours. She concluded:
"It is a mile to the City Hall (Guildhall). If the
caterpillar sets off at noon on Monday he will
reach the City Hall at 6 o'clock on Thursday
morning. This does not allow for meals, traffic
or sleeping." (Subsequently she discovered from
her brother that these caterpillars' span of life is
much shorter than this!)

7-7. Geometry — Shapes

Reference has already been made to the necessity
for extensive experience with the varied three-
dimensional shapes of the environment before
studying two-dimensional shapes. Children will
help to make a large collection of containers and
cartons — and will enjoy searching for a variety
of natural shapes: flowers, leaves, shells and fossils.
The first thing they want to do with these collections is to play with them; for example, to make
models by glueing boxes together.

Some 5-year-olds, given this opportunity for
the first time, showed considerable imagination.
One girl made two boxes into a loud speaker and
asked her *daughter,* lost in a large store, to come
to the loudspeaker where she would find her
mother.

Covering the models by pasting newsprint
on them makes the models far stronger. They can
be made attractive for exhibition by allowing
children to paint them with thick powder paint.
When a child has spent some time making three-
dimensional models of his house, a van, a boat,
etc., he begins to think about some two-dimensional
shapes for himself.

A six-year-old who had made a complicated
model of a house, draped at every window, topped
with a square chimney, and fitted with a garden
set, was able to make freehand drawings of every
elevation and of the plan or plot (as seen from an
aircraft). Each sketch showed a good judgment
of proportion and an excellent knowledge of
two-dimensional shapes.

Sorting 3-Dimensional Shapes

When 5-or 6-year-olds are encouraged to decide
for themselves how to sort or classify a collection,
they invariably sort by colours first. Later, they
will begin to sort according to shape, although
they may not always be able to describe what
they have done. At this stage you can help them
with vocabulary, introducing words as a child
needs them.

Some deaf five-year-olds had made a large
collection of containers. Their teacher drew a
square, a rectangle and a circle on the floor and
watched the children to see what they would do.
They put cubes in the square, the other cuboids in
the rectangle and cylinders in the circle. A box
with a square cross-section made a girl hesitate.
At last she decided that the box belonged in the
rectangle because 4 faces were rectangles and
only 2 were squares.

Children sort balls, cylinders and boxes, and
discover, by experiment, their characteristic
behaviour: balls always roll, cylinders roll in some
positions, cuboids tip over but do not roll, etc.
They will also sort each set into subsets: long or
tall boxes, flat boxes, etc. When children are able
to sort all the cubes from a set of cuboids they
are usually able to recognize a square because
they distinguish cubes by their square faces.
Unless children are given sufficient experience
with three-dimensional shapes they may find
difficulty in abstracting the idea of a square.

An 8-year-old-boy was asked to make the
largest square he could from a set of square tiles.
He persistently made rectangles until his teacher
showed him a nest of cubes of increasing sizes.
She asked him to find other cubes to go with the
set. When she was sure that he could identify
cubes she asked him, once more, to make the
largest square he could. This time he was able
to make a square but said he would like to try
the problem again next day as he needed more
practice!

7-8. Pictorial Representation, Block or Column Graphs

It is essential for young children to use
3-dimensional material which is as realistic as
possible: model cars and vans in a traffic survey
(see the film *Maths Alive*), or portraits of themselves for graphs of birthdays.

Number of children in family.

Common Base Line

The first time children make a graph they usually do not start with a common base line. When they begin to compare numbers you can ask them if they can think of a way of arranging the coloured cubes, beads or boxes they are using which would make comparison easy.

Equal Units

Children take some time to realize the need for equal units. A teacher of 8-year-olds had suggested that the children should prepare an assignment about their families. As a preliminary step they were given pieces of paper of equal size so they could draw portraits of themselves. To the teacher's dismay, after the children had drawn their portraits and cut them out, the portraits were different sizes. She watched them glue these to the mounting paper. No child thought of starting from a common base line!

While children must be given freedom to think for themselves in this kind of representation, nevertheless, the teacher must ask questions to persuade children to suggest for themselves the necessity both for equal units and for a common base line. For example, what can we do to avoid counting every time to see how many more have 2 in the family than 3? Once this has been discussed, if coloured inch squares and inch-squared paper are provided, children seldom have further difficulty. These preliminary experiences should not be hurried if children are to be encouraged to discover and to use their imagination.

Chapter 8

Mathematics and Related
Activities for Upper Grades

8-1	Weight and Density	143
8-2	Ratio and Proportion	147
8-3	Statistics	148
8-4	Geometry—Properties of Shapes	149
8-5	Geometry—Congruence and Symmetry	153
8-6	Geometry—Similarity	154
8-7	Limits and Infinity	157
8-8	Graphs and Algebra	158
8-9	Sets and Relations	160

Mathematics and Related Activities for Upper Grades

In this chapter we will concern ourselves with mathematics and related activities that are usually considered to be part of the curriculum in the upper elementary grades. It is often possible however, to give introductory experiences for these topics to younger children. Occasionally in this chapter, we will make references to these experiences for younger children.

Co-operation between the primary and secondary school is extremely important if the transfer of graduating primary students is to be a smooth one. Understanding each other's curriculum and methods as well as evaluating students' work therefore assumes great importance. To this end, intervisitation among teachers of similar and varying age groups should be encouraged. Many school systems now provide release time for teachers to visit colleagues in the same school or in the same school system. In several communities, intervisitation is contingent upon the visiting teacher inviting his host teacher back to observe in his own classroom. This avoids the tendency of treating any one teacher as an expert.

Aside from the co-operation and mutual respect fostered by this program, intervisitation is valuable in that it encourages a pooling of ideas and methods and shared solving of problems both common and unique.

8-1. Weight and Density

Weight is not an easy topic for young children; therefore, a variety of experiences are essential. One preliminary experience that is particularly useful is that of using a balance type scale of the suspension type.

Children are usually first interested in making the scale pans go up and down. Some young five-year-olds used wooden cubes of all sizes until their pet hamster, in the other pan, was as high as he could be. He showed no concern and continued to wash his face throughout the *weighing*. When they were asked if they could just balance the hamster, one seized the crossbar and first held it horizontal and then released it. Another boy then removed all the cubes so that the hamster came to earth with a bump. These children were clearly at the play stage of weighing.

Only after adequate experience will the words *heavier* and *lighter* have meaning for children. They will then begin to use these words in the right context. "Find two things heavier than the toy truck and two things lighter." "Can you find anything which weighs the same as the truck?" "How many bottle caps balance a marble?" "Which is heavier, a cup of beans or a cup of rice?" These questions represent different stages, each of which requires adequate experience.

Experience with a seesaw (a plank of wood and a brick) is also useful in developing the idea of balance. The following example of children's work illustrates how difficult this concept of *balancing* is.

*A teacher provided his seven-year-old class
with a plank placed over a brick and stood
on one end himself. ''Can you lift me?'' he asked.
All the children were eager to try and each,
in turn, stood on the other end. When all had failed
to lift the teacher they decided they needed
to jump on the other end. Once more they tried
and failed. At last a boy who had been looking
at the brick from the side (as in the fig.) asked,
''Can I move the brick?'' He did so and showed
that he could now lift the teacher easily. This boy
became interested in weighing and made a
home-made balance himself from a piece of wood.
He experimented for some time.*

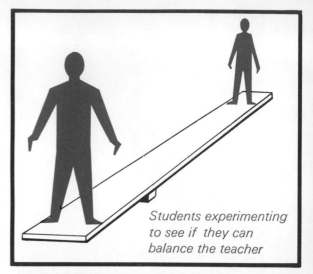

Students experimenting
to see if they can
balance the teacher

The teacher did not follow this up. A month
later another teacher tried the same experiment
with this group of children. To his surprise,
the children responded exactly as before,
first standing, then jumping on the other end,
to no purpose.

Evidently this is a difficult idea for young
children, who may need far more experience and
discussion before the concept is understood.
Children can use a seesaw again and again
without learning anything from it. They require
experience, questions from adults, and a chance
to discuss their suggestions. A child has made
great progress towards understanding when
he says that the heavy child must sit nearer the
middle (point of balance, fulcrum) than the light
child to balance him or we must move the
brick nearer to the teacher to balance him.

A child's first experience with springs will
probably be that of using elastic. A few elastic
bands can be looped one through another and
attached to a plastic beaker as a scale pan for
adding weight. Modern scales, which work by
means of compression and extension springs,
present real difficulty to pupils, since the springs
can be felt but not seen when pressure is applied.
Therefore, varied experience should be provided
with springs of all kinds: fragile and strong, long
and short, extension and compression.

Each school, and if possible each classroom,
needs to have a varied collection of compression
and extension scales. ''Can you find out how
these scales work? Could you make one for
yourself?'' were the questions one teacher gave
his class. A box of springs and elastics were

Using standard units of weight to weigh an object

available to the students. These pupils soon discovered the relationship between the weight added and the extension of the spring. This helped them to make their own scales for weighing.

Standard Units of Weight

It is useful for each school to have a set of standard weights. Students need to handle them to get the *feel* of them, to discover the relationship between one weight and another, and to discover the sequence. Labels on packaged goods are often confusing. We use 8 oz. and ½ lb. so indiscriminately that these equivalences cause considerable confusion until students have discovered the relationship through various experiences. In England, cooking with a recipe is an excellent way of giving pupils purposeful activity in weighing.

Metric Weights

Students can find, from firsthand experience, the equivalent of a kilogram in pounds and ounces. They can also find the gram equivalents of a pound and of an ounce. The weights of some packaged goods are expressed in grams as well as in ounces. These can be checked from a ready reckoner graph made by using the equivalent of a pound in grams. Pupils enjoy planning a holiday or vacation and deciding what weight of candies, apples, peaches, coffee, butter, ham, etc. they would need to buy.

Density

Many adults lack the necessary experience to understand this difficult concept. It is probably not until the age of 12 or 13 that most students really understand density. This comes as the result of many varied experiences which begin at a very early age, often before the child starts school. We must learn that volume and weight are separate properties. Some large objects are light (polystyrene blocks) and some small objects are heavy (magnets, weights). Sorting heavy and light objects focusses attention on this characteristic. Discussion with pupils is essential during or after such experiences to give them the opportunity to put these experiences into words.

Another way of sorting objects is to find out if they float or sink. Since water has a fascination for all children the discovery that some objects float while others sink is an interesting experience.

Such experience brings children directly in contact with the idea of density: the comparison of the weight of an object with the weight of an equal volume of water.

Often at the age of 9 or 10, students discover that a metal foil pie case will float, but if it is crumpled up into a ball and the air is pressed out it will sink. This often provokes the question: "Why does an iron boat float?" to which pupils give many and varied suggestions, most of which can be tested experimentally. The child can be encouraged to devise experiments himself.

Here are three examples of students' work which focus attention on the difficulty of the concept of density:

1/ (This example is shown in the film *Maths Alive*.) Some girls were weighing a beaker of sugar, a beaker of tea, a beaker of flour, etc. They needed a ¼ ounce weight, but the smallest weight they had was ½ ounce. After some discussion they made an identical model of the brass weight in plasticene and prepared to cut this in half. Before they did so, the teacher, who had been watching, asked them to describe what they had done. As they did so, they realized that the plasticene model did not weigh ½ ounce. They then weighed ½ ounce of plasticene and cut that in two, checking by weighing.

They made a graph of their results which included the weight of the beaker. "Will the weight of the beaker make any difference?" the teacher asked. "No," the girls replied, "because it's the same beaker all the time." The teacher pointed out that the beaker was not made of the same material as sugar, tea, flour, etc. The girls were slow to accept this idea (so, too, are adults). Each held an empty beaker in her hands. "Anyway, it doesn't weigh anything," they said. They were surprised to find that a plastic beaker weighed an ounce.

2/ A boy was asked to find which of two pieces of metal was the larger. "At first I thought I'd measure the surface area," he wrote, "but I couldn't because one piece had a hole in it." Then he decided to measure the amount of air space each occupied. "But I don't know how to do that, so I'll have to measure the space each takes up in water." In order to do this the boy had to make and graduate his own measuring jar and measure the amount by which the water rose for each piece. This experiment led the boy to put into words his own idea of density: "If you wanted to find the largest of several pieces of metal, and they were all the same metal, I think weight would tell you."

3/ Some eleven-year-old boys were first estimating and then finding the volume of a number of large pieces of rock. They devised a method for themselves. They stood a bucket of water in a bowl and then filled the bucket completely (one boy watched to make sure that no water was spilt in the basin). They then lowered a stone suspended on a piece of string carefully into the water. The overflow for each stone was poured into a measuring jug. The teacher then asked them to find out how many times as heavy as water stone is. After some discussion they decided to weigh the water which overflowed for a stone of weight 3 lbs. The water weighed 1¼ lbs. "Stone is more than twice and less than three times as heavy as water," they said.

This experiment illustrates the difference between density and specific gravity. One is a rate — the other a ratio. *Three times as heavy as water* is a ratio and is called the specific gravity of the substance, about 3 in this instance. The density of a substance is the weight per unit volume; that is, the weight of 1 cubic inch, 1 cubic foot (used for timber of all kinds), or 1 cubic centimetre. It is useful to remember that the weight of a cubic foot of water is 1000 ounces. The weight of 1 cubic centimetre of water is 1 gram. Rates involve two different units: 1000 ounces per cubic foot, 1 gram per cubic centimetre. Density is a difficult concept because it is concerned with two variables: volume and weight. The girls who made a plasticene replica of the ½ ounce weight were assuming that equal volumes of brass and plasticene would weigh the same, ½ ounce. Weights and volumes of different substances cannot be compared simultaneously; one of these variables must be fixed. The reply of a six-year-old to the question "Which is heavier, a cup of rice or a cup of peas?" was natural for that age: "I guess peas because they're bigger."

Comparison

Some students were comparing the weight of a cup of beans with a cup of water. The cup of beans appeared lighter than the cup of water. One boy promptly dropped some of the beans into the water. They sank immediately. "I knew they would. Why did they weigh lighter than the water?" he asked. The teacher, who began to have doubts herself, asked the boy to try to find the answer himself. After some thought he said, "We're weighing air in the beans." "How can you get rid of the air?" he was asked. All the children had noticed that beans absorb water — so they filled a cup with dry beans, poured water to the brim, and quickly poured the water off and weighed it. They compared this weight with that of a full cup of water. They were surprised to find how large the fraction of air was — and repeated the experiment with marbles and rice.

Estimation of their own volume in pints and cubic feet is of great interest to secondary students. Find the volume of your body in pints. Estimates are wild at first, but when students are asked whether they float or sink in water and compare their density with that of water, they usually realise that the density of the human body is very nearly the same as that of water. If they weigh water, they find that a gallon weighs about 10 lbs. Using this fact, every 10 lbs. of the human body occupies about 1 gallon.

Firm practical foundations will help studies of flotation. Six-year-olds who have experienced their legs "floating" in the bath or the upthrust from a cuboid of polystyrene while swimming, will often guess that objects (like rocks) will weigh less when suspended in water than in air. The same question seems to present more difficulty to children of 9; children often guess that stones will weigh more in water "because water presses harder than air." Many adults are also confused because Archimedes' Principle was learned by rote (or by teacher demonstration). Yet some ten-year-old boys were thrilled to discover for themselves that the "loss" in weight of rocks suspended in water (the upthrust of the water) was about the same as the weight of water each rock displaced (i.e. the weight of its own volume of water). For comparison of densities of liquids experience is also important, e.g. cream will float on milk.

Conservation

Piaget has drawn attention to another difficult concept concerning density. Identical cubes (or cylinders) made of different metals are given to students to examine. "If these cubes are put in that jar of water what will happen?" they are asked. If the reply is: "The water will rise," the question continues: "If each cube is placed in the water in turn, will the level rise by the same amount or by different amounts for each cube?" With inadequate experience, the answer "by different amounts" will often be given.

Teachers of mathematics at the secondary level often leave the topic of density and specific gravity to the scientists. However, problems involving density and specific gravity are practical examples of rate and ratio. Since the concept is a difficult one, it should be studied using different approaches, particularly if the co-operation of the science department is enlisted.

8-2. Ratio and Proportion

Some of the children's work shown in Chapter 7 has involved ratio; the circumference/diameter relationship of circles is an example of a ratio. In many of their comparisons of body measurements pupils will approximate simple ratios:

Your waist measurement is about twice your neck measurement (2:1), and your height is approximately equal to the width of your outstretched arms from fingertip to fingertip (1:1).

Some eleven-year-olds were having their first experience of practical measurement. They had been asked to measure and record the lengths of the sides of various rectangles in the room. They were then asked to estimate the ratio of the sides of the classroom door. "6 to 1," they suggested.

The teacher then asked: "How long would the chalkboard be if its sides were in the ratio 6:1? What would the width of the table be if its sides were in the ratio 6:1?" The girls found this quite difficult at first so the ratio was changed, first to 2:1 and then to 4:1. With these simple ratios the whole class understood and problems could be solved without actual measurement. This avoided calculations involving complicated

Discovering great circle distances on a globe

measurements, and focussed attention on the concept of ratio and proportion.

A group of eleven-year-olds collected various scale models of aircraft, locomotives, cars and boats. Using the scale given in the catalogue (often $1/72$, sometimes $1/20$), they calculated the dimensions of the actual objects and drew life-size plans in the school yard. They were able to check some of the results for cars. Their teacher also asked them to discover the scale of some models of cars by comparison with the original.

A group of students in Britain collected envelopes from letters they received during the summer holiday. Using a railway map of Britain (scale 16 miles to 1 inch) they calculated how far the letters had travelled.

A girl in Chicago had received an air mail letter from an uncle in London. Using a globe, she stretched a piece of fine string from London to Chicago. There was some discussion about the route. The string was pulled taut. At first the children called this the "straight" distance and then saw that the string did not appear straight — so they called this the "direct distance, as the crow flies." This led to an investigation of balls, spheres and eventually of "great circle distances" drawn on the balls. Ultimately, they made a ready reckoner graph from which the actual mileage between any two places on the globe could be read off directly when the "direct string" distance was known.

8-3. Statistics

One of the fastest growing fields of mathematics, yet one of the least understood by the common man, is that of statistics. For this reason any experiences or activities of this kind that you can plan for your pupils are particularly beneficial. It has been our experience that even young children can understand some of the basic concepts of statistics: collecting data, organizing data, representing or displaying the data, and finding how large a sample must be if it is to be representative. Older pupils are able to understand some of the more advanced concepts of statistics: central tendencies (mean, mode, median), deviation from the mean, standard deviation, distribution, frequency and biased sampling.

Distribution, Mean (Average) and Mode

In a junior school in Britain, the older pupils were asked to devise simple enquiries which all children in the school could help to make. The following questions are some of those asked by the older pupils for the other children to answer. Each group made an illustrated book about their investigation.

1/ To find out if children staying to school dinner are heavier or lighter than children going home for dinner. (Children going home to dinner proved to be much lighter, to the surprise of the group investigating this problem.)

2/ To find out if boys have more or less pocket money than girls of the same age.

3/ To compare the weights of children living in houses with the weights of children living in flats.

4/ To find out whether boys have more teeth than girls of the same age.

5/ To find out whether boys and girls living in flats have different pets than boys and girls living in houses.

The information was ordered and the results were represented in a variety of ways. The results of the investigations often surprised the children and they asked, and solved, further questions in their search for answers.

The enquiries carried out by these older pupils often led to the calculation of the average (or arithmetic mean). The mode (most frequently occurring item of data) and distribution were discussed in every enquiry made and there were frequent references to these statistical measures.

Average (Arithmetic Mean)

The examples pupils are set to do "for practice" are sometimes very artificial. Measurement affords many realistic opportunities in which an average has a purpose. For example, pupils often suggest "pacing" when they have no other means of measuring a long distance, and if they are comparing two lengths they do not need to know the actual length of a pace. When they want to know an actual distance, then they will have to know the actual length of a pace. This is not as easy as it sounds, because when pacing, we all tend to exaggerate the length of our pace.

How many paces do we need to take in order to find the (average) length of normal pace? Get suggestions from the students (10? 20? 30? 50? 100?). Ask them to try and check for various numbers. If you then ask the students to devise another method of finding the length of individual paces they may suggest counting the number of paces they take to cover, say, 20 yards.

Coin-Tossing Cumulative Graph

An unusual representation of a coin-tossing experiment was undertaken by some ten-year-olds who tossed a coin 100 times. For each new toss, they made a "cumulative" total of heads and tails and expressed each as a percentage of the total number of tosses. Here is their record of some of the tosses.

Number of toss	Result	Tails total	%	Heads total	%
1	T	1	100	0	0
2	H	1	50	1	50
3	H	1	33⅓	2	66⅔
4	H	1	25	3	75
5	T	2	40	3	60

They were interested to see how the percentage of each approached 50 as the number of tosses approached 100.

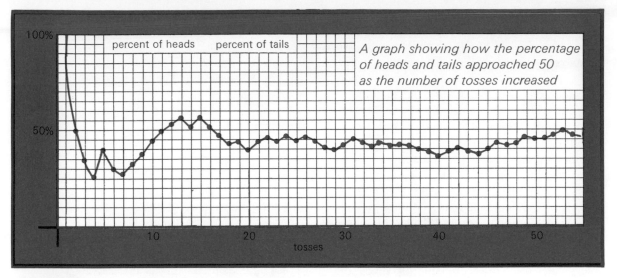

A graph showing how the percentage
of heads and tails approached 50
as the number of tosses increased

A graph showing the total score of a pair of dice

Dice: Expected Frequencies

Some twelve- and thirteen-year-olds had tossed
a die 480 times and recorded the score. They
represented the results on a block graph on which
they also entered the expected frequency of each
number (80). They then repeated this with 2 dice,
recording the total score each time. They were
surprised to find how near the expected frequencies the results were. (We suggest you
make a table of all possible scores and work out
the expected frequencies with pupils. Remember
that there are 36 possible combinations. There are
6 combinations that give a score of seven,
while only 1 combination that gives a score of two.)
The group then made a seven-faced "device"
and recorded the scores obtained by tossing this
200 times. Their results made them decide that
their homemade device was decidely biased!

8-4. Geometry – Properties of Shapes

There are many properties of shapes that can be
used to devise experiences for students. In this
section we will discuss volume, rigidity and angles
of polygons. In addition, we will present some
paper folding activity.

Measuring Solid Shapes

Given encouragement, students will measure
solid shapes in a variety of ways. Measurement
of surface area is not as easily calculated as
measurement of volume.

149

The following example illustrates how two groups of students solved the same problem. They were given a set of three open rectangular containers. These were specially made of paper of the same thickness and had the same volume. The students were asked to find out anything they could about the containers by matching or measuring. One group measured the length, breadth and height of each and multiplied these together to obtain the volume. The other group filled one with sand and tipped this into each of the other containers to test their guess that each container held the same amount. The teacher then asked the groups if they could find which container had the greatest surface area. The first group used the measurements they had made. Once more the second group employed a more direct method; they weighed the empty containers and announced that the long thin one had the most surface area. The two groups were then brought together to compare and discuss their methods.

Experimenting with Two-Dimensional Shapes

A group consisting of 9-, 10-, 11- and 12-year-olds were given a set of tongue depressors or spatulas and thumb tacks. The students were asked to make shapes with the tongue depressors and thumb tacks. The shapes they made included the following:

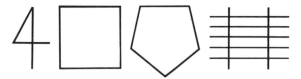

The students noticed immediately that only the first of the shapes was fixed. The younger ones thought that if they put in enough thumb tacks they could fix the shape, and were surprised to find that this was not so. At this stage the tongue depressors proved unsatisfactory and cardboard strips were introduced. The strips were made of stiff 5" cardboard — ½" wide each with two holes punched ¼" from the ends. Paper fasteners were supplied for fastening strips together. Subsequently 8" strips, with holes punched at ½" intervals as far as the centre, and one hole ¼" from the other end, were made available. A ten-year-old then made a triangle and was excited to

find that she had made another fixed or rigid shape. She then tried to make the square rigid. When she used a short strip the square became

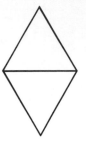

a diamond and it was at this point that the teacher suggested using the 8-inch-strips. Some of the group then made a set of regular shapes with 3, 4, 5, 6, . . ., 12 sides and set about making these rigid, using the longer strips. More than one method was used for each shape. For example, rigid pentagons were obtained by both methods shown in the figure.

Eventually the twelve-year-olds decided to follow a pattern, starting all the *stiffening strips* from one corner. This showed clearly that the triangle was a rigid shape. From the set of regular shapes they obtained the following sequences:

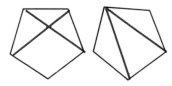

Number of sides and corners	Number of stiffening strips	Number of triangles
3	0	1
4	1	2
5	2	3

They immediately noticed the patterns and predicted "straight line" graphs. Later they realized that the graphs were not continuous because they could not make regular polygons with 3½ sides.

Sum of the Angles of Triangles and of Polygons

Students can discover this unexpected and exciting result for themselves in a variety of ways. First they need to realize, through varied experiences, that an angle is associated with a rotation.

The first angle they will meet is a right angle or quarter revolution. They can make this for themselves by folding a piece of paper twice and they can then test the corners of the chalkboard and room to see if these are right angles.

After testing the angles of a square, some pupils discovered the sum of the angles of a right-angled isosceles triangle by folding the square in half. Similarly, they cut a rectangle and discovered that the sum of the angles in each triangle was also two right angles. Finally, they experimented with regular (and later scalene) triangles, fitting these together. They discovered that the 3 angles of a triangle fitted together to make a straight line.

One of the best ways of finding the sum of the angles is to have students cut the angles off paper triangles and polygons, then paste the angles adjacent to each other.

A class of 12-year-olds had each constructed 3 large triangles: one regular (equilateral), one isosceles and one scalene. They were asked to fold the corners of the scalene triangle so that the vertices met and the angles were adjacent. The teacher suggested they try first with the regular triangle. They managed this easily and found that the three vertices met at the middle point of one side. In the figures the folds are designated. The children's attention was diverted for some time because they made other interesting discoveries about the points P and Q and the area of the triangle. They soon realized that the sum of the three angles of the triangle was two right angles because the outer arms were in a straight line. Some then returned to the scalene triangle; others experimented with the isosceles triangle.

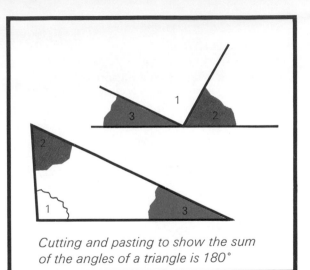

Cutting and pasting to show the sum of the angles of a triangle is 180°

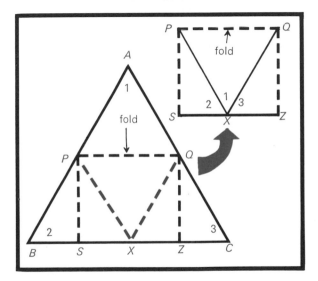

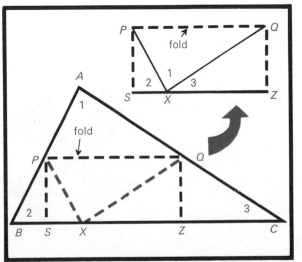

Angles of Regular Polygons

A large class of 10- and 11-year-olds noticed the pattern in the figure and made these observations: A regular triangle has 3 sides and angles of 60°, and a regular hexagon has 6 sides and angles of 120°. They asked: "Is there a pattern?" Their teacher suggested that they explore this further. They made the table shown but could not find

Number of sides	Angle
3	60°
4	90°
5	108°
6	120°
7	$128^4/_9$°
8	135°

a pattern so they drew a graph. At first they thought they would find a turning point — so they drew a graph which included the angle of a polygon of 240 sides! "It looks as though the graph is going on forever, getting nearer to 180°," one said. They became so absorbed with the pattern that one group considered polygons with 450 million sides! "When we saw the pattern we realised we never should reach 180°," they wrote.

Some ten-year-olds first made regular polygons by constructing and cutting out, in coloured gummed paper, sets of isosceles triangles. For the octagon, they made the vertical angles of the 8 triangles 45° (360° ÷ 8) and the equal sides 1". They cut these in two colours and gummed them as shown in the figure. They found the base angles of each triangle to be 67½° so the interior angles were each 2 × 67½° or 135°. They were also interested in the table from which they discovered the constant product pattern. When asked what a graph would show they hesitated, but were quite sure it would not be a straight line.

Number of sides	angle at centre
3	120°
4	90°
5	72°
6	60°
8	45°
9	40°
10	36°

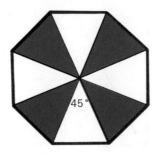

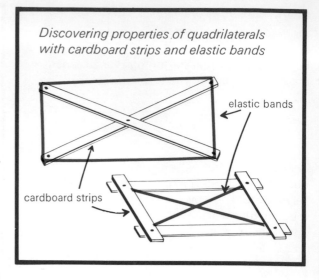

Discovering properties of quadrilaterals with cardboard strips and elastic bands

elastic bands

cardboard strips

Experimenting with Squares, Rectangles, Rhombuses and Parallelograms

This can be done in many ways with a variety of materials: paperfolding, square and rectangular frameworks of cardboard strips, and elastic bands. Paperfolding gives a quick means of discovery and has the added advantage that the process can be reversed.

Some pupils experimented with folded paper, cutting corners through first one and then two folds. Before they unfolded the corners they had cut off, their teacher asked them to say what they thought the shape would be. They were surprised to find that the cut across a double fold gave a diamond (rhombus). "What would you have to do to get a square?" the teacher asked. The pupils experimented before they answered: "Make an equal cut." By this, they meant that the ends of the cut had to be equidistant from the corner. They were soon familiar with the similarities and differences of squares and rhombuses. They also discovered resemblances and differences between rectangles and parallelograms, using cardboard frameworks. They made skeleton three-dimensional shapes to see what they could discover about these.

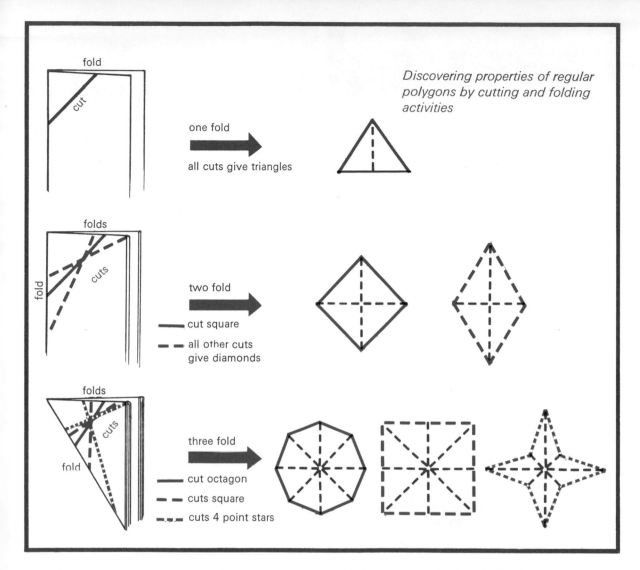

Discovering properties of regular polygons by cutting and folding activities

fold

cut

one fold

all cuts give triangles

folds

fold

cuts

two fold

—— cut square

--- all other cuts give diamonds

folds

cuts

fold

three fold

—— cut octagon

--- cuts square

–·– cuts 4 point stars

8-5. Geometry – Congruence and Symmetry

Most of us think of congruent triangles when the word congruence is mentioned. This is because we were introduced to the abstract triangle before we had had wider experience of the idea of congruence in our everyday environment. In fact, we come in contact with many pleasing examples of congruence: the repeating patterns of textiles, of tiled floors, of light fittings, of ironwork.

Symmetry – Mirror Image (Uni-Axial or Bilateral)

Symmetrical shapes give further examples of congruence. Children recognize symmetry at an early age. A five-year-old boy, who had dropped a paint blot on a sheet of paper by mistake and folded it to throw the paper away, was so delighted with the pattern he had made that he began to experiment with more than one colour. The teacher took advantage of this "accident" and asked the children to collect shapes that were like Stephen's pattern. They collected leaves, flowers, insects, textile patterns and tiles. They soon found that some flowers "could be folded in half more than one way" and the teacher asked them to record in how many ways each shape could be folded in half.

Students have many natural classroom experiences which lead them to produce symmetrical shapes, particularly by paperfolding and cutting. A small rectangular hand mirror and tracing paper will help them in their investigations.

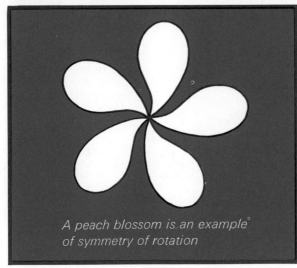

*A peach blossom is an example
of symmetry of rotation*

Symmetry – Rotation

Some nine-year-olds made a collection of wild flowers and then began to sort them into sets according to their colours (white, pink, and yellow). They next sorted the flowers according to the number of petals each had. They found the largest set contained the five-petalled flowers. While sorting the flowers they found that some had "mirror image symmetry" (one axis only), while most flowers had two or more axes of symmetry. One flower with five petals did not have mirror image symmetry at all. The teacher asked his pupils to cut a cardboard template of one petal and to use this to make the flower. They found they could do this by pinning the template at the pointed end and turning (rotating) it to five different positions. They then made a collection of shapes which had "rotational symmetry." These included capital letters, numerals and geometric shapes.

Symmetry of Geometric Shapes

A group of nine- and ten-year-olds discussed and made diagrams of the axes of symmetry of various geometric shapes: triangles, various quadrilaterals, regular pentagons, etc. They were puzzled by the rectangle. They had been quite sure that the two triangles made by the diagonal were identical until they folded the rectangle along the diagonal. The teacher suggested that they cut the rectangle in two along the diagonal and see whether the two triangles could be superimposed. After some experimenting, the students found that the triangles could be superimposed by rotating one through 2 right angles (or half a turn).

The Kaleidoscope

At the secondary level, geometrical properties of reflection (correspondences of lines and angles) can be discovered by the students using a small mirror fixed to stand vertically.[†] The various types of kaleidoscopes on the market fascinate adults as well as children. Using two hinged mirrors and a pin with a coloured head as object, students can discover for themselves the relationship between the angle formed by the mirrors and the total number of pins (object and images) seen. The graph is an interesting discontinuous one. Various polygons can also be made by drawing a line to join one point on each mirror.

8-6. Geometry – Similarity

The property of similarity preserves shape, but not size. Scale models and maps are applications of the principle of similarity. Six- and seven-year-olds have an intuitive awareness of proportion when model-making; they cut and glue boxes together until the model looks right to them.

[†]A rectangular piece of transparent plastic will also work and has the additional advantage that the user can see through the plastic to pencil the observed image.

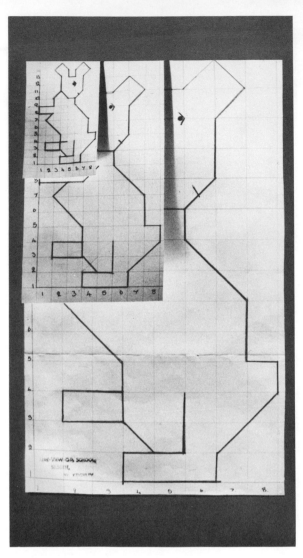

Similar figures

How Cubes Grow

Building a sequence of larger cubes using unit cubes is a profitable experience. Some seven-year-olds are able to build a cube with edges twice that of the unit cube. Adults, as well as children, usually stop at one layer in their first attempt to build a cube with edges twice as long as a unit cube; but soon realize that a second layer is required.

How Cuboids Grow

Adults and children find it much harder to build a sequence of similar cuboids using unit cuboids. Unit cuboids might be a collection of identical thumbtack containers, felt-tip pen boxes or Cuisenaire rods. Pupils need experience with containers of various shapes before they can build, without hesitation, a sequence of cuboids with edges 2, 3 and 4 times those of the unit cuboid. The experience of building larger cuboids from smaller cuboids is essential for an understanding of similarity.

Similarity in Two Dimensions

Pupils also need the experience of making a set of squares, using unit squares; a set of triangles (regular, isosceles and scalene), using unit triangles; sets of rectangles; rhombuses; etc. In fact, many shapes which will tessellate can be used. Encourage them to look for patterns in the similar shapes they make.

Similarity Sequences of Volume and Area

A class kept various pets in the classroom: mice, guinea pigs and hamsters. They commented that the mouse seemed to be eating most of the day, so the teacher asked them if they could find out exactly how much the mouse ate. Students kept careful records for a month and found that the mouse ate the equivalent of about half of its weight (1 ounce) in food every day and that the guinea pig ate about one quarter of its weight each day. Robert found that his baby sister, who weighed 8 lbs., was fed 5 ounces 6 times a day; about one quarter of her weight, he calculated. He kept a record of the food he ate himself and found this to be 4½ lbs., about $1/25$ of his weight (112 lbs.).

The students discussed possible reasons for the difference and eventually decided that this could be due to heat loss. They found the skin area of a girl and divided this by her weight, and the skin area of a mouse and divided this by its weight. The two rates they obtained were 5½ to 1 and 26 to 1. To help them to understand this the teacher suggested that they investigate the "skin area"/weight (or volume) relationship of a set of cubes of increasing size. They made the following table. They called the final column "the number of squares to each cube."

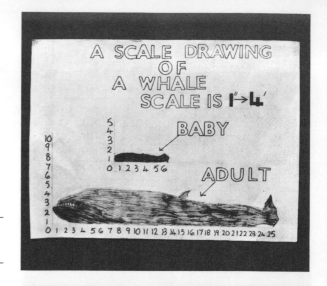

	Edge of cube	Volume or number of cubes (V)	Skin Area or number of squares	Area / Volume or number of squares to each cube
	1	1	6	6
(Baby 2 ft.)	2	8	24	3
	3	27	54	2
(Child 4 ft.)	4	64	96	$^3/_2$
	5	125	150	$^6/_5$
(Man 6 ft.)	6	216	216	1

From the table the pupils realized that the skin-area/volume rate for a baby was about three times that of a 6 ft. man. This helped them to understand why a baby has to eat one quarter of its weight in food. They drew graphs of the volume/edge and skin-area/edge and this led them to continue the table and its graph. "Is it because a cube has six faces that we get such an interesting result when the edge is 6 units?" they asked. They graphed their results in the final column against those in the first column. This graph showed clearly how the rate decreased as the edge increased.

A nine-year-old asked her friends which was the largest mammal. Some said the blue whale, others disagreed. Many books were consulted before they settled for the blue whale. In order to get some idea of its size, the children measured 100 ft. on the playground. They expressed the length of the blue whale in 100-foot units. They then measured the height of the classroom and discovered that the body of the whale would be the same height as their two-story school. The heaviest weight they could imagine was a 112 lb. sack of coal, so they expressed the weight of the whale in sacks of coal.

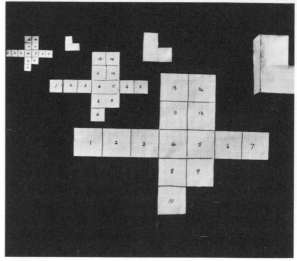

Similar figures showing ratio and proportion

It is important that students' experiences should give them the opportunity to discover those shapes which are always similar: cubes, spheres, squares, circles. How many small balls would occupy the same space as the large ball? What measurements do you need to take to find out? (Children and adults find this difficult, but it is a question which can be solved practically and then discussed.) How many small cylinders will fill the large cylinder? Estimate before you experiment, then measure to see if you were right. How many small cylinders did you need?

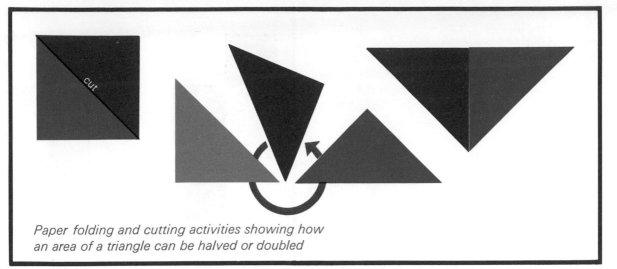

*Paper folding and cutting activities showing how
an area of a triangle can be halved or doubled*

Experiences like the one indicated above will
help students to understand this concept of
similarity and to establish for themselves those
conditions which make, for example, cylinders
similar in shape. They also need experience in two
dimensions. What happens to the circumference
and the area of a circle when its diameter is
doubled? Would a similar result be obtained for
any other shape; for instance, a rectangle when its
edges are doubled?

Ratio and Proportion

Similarity in mathematical shapes provides excellent experience in ratio and proportion. We are
constantly comparing the ratio of corresponding
lengths when testing for similarity. To test two
rectangles for similarity find the ratio of the lengths
and widths. If the two ratios are the same
we know that the two rectangles are in the same
proportion and we say the two rectangles are
similar. If, for example, we double the length only
and forget to double the width we obtain a shape
which is a caricature! Try this with shapes other
than rectangles and see the interesting results.

Since the shape of two objects must be identical
for the shapes to be mathematically similar, the
corresponding angles of the shapes must be the
same. This has been true of the geometrical shapes
we have considered: rectangles, squares, triangles
and hexagons.

8-7. Limits and Infinity

These two ideas are very important in mathematics
at secondary and university levels, but children also
have experiences leading to these ideas. For
example, once they can count with understanding
they soon discover that counting is unending and,
later, that any fraction has an unending sequence
of equivalent fractions.

In reply to the question: "What is the largest
number you know?", an 8-year-old said, "If I tell
you one number now, the next second I could tell
you a number one more than that and so on
forever."

Spatial Examples of Limits and of Unending Sequences

In Mathematics we are constantly "looking both
ways." We continue our investigations until either
some physical condition causes us to stop or we
find that the sequence is unending. This is a good
introduction to the idea of a limit and of infinity.

Some pupils were asked to make the largest
possible square from a sheet of paper (without
actually measuring). After some false starts, the
pupils matched the short side against the long
side and cut off the spare piece. In doing this they
had folded the square along its diagonal and
obtained a triangle. They described this as a right-
angled triangle because the angles of a square are
right angles. They also said that two of its sides
were equal. "How do you know?" asked the
teacher. To show her, they matched the equal sides;

157

in doing this they obtained still another isosceles right-angled triangle. "What is happening to the area?" asked the teacher. "It's halving all the time: $1/2$, $1/4$, $1/8$, $1/16$, $1/32$," they said as they continued folding with much excitement. Cathy said: "We're going to get a very wee triangle in the end, but we shan't ever get to nothing at all." Scott remarked that as his triangle got smaller the paper got thicker until it was too thick to fold. At this stage the teacher asked them to unfold the paper to the first square and to cut it along the diagonal. As they unfolded they said the area was now doubling. The pupils were excited by the pattern of folds and the pattern of larger and larger triangles and larger and larger squares. They had recognized the sequence of similar right-angled isosceles triangles. She asked them to see if they could make a larger triangle, of the same shape as the others, using the two triangular halves of the square. "Join with a friend and see if you can make a still larger triangle using your four triangles," the teacher suggested. Janet shouted in her enthusiasm: "Me and Scott have done it," and went on to combine with another pair of children to make a similar triangle using 8 pieces. "This could go on forever," she said.

A similar sequence was obtained by some nine-year-olds (a very backward group at computation), starting with a large square sheet of paper and joining the midpoints of adjacent sides. At first they called the new shape a diamond, but after turning it around, they convinced themselves it was a square. (At a higher level or with more experienced students, this statement would require mathematical justification.) After repeating the process several times, a girl said: "We shall never quite get to the centre." When asked if they could make a larger square than the initial one they took a square of paper into the school yard and announced that they could continue this process until the largest square filled the yard. (Backwardness in computation often does not hinder students' mathematical insight with shapes. Frequently, success with shapes gives them encouragement to make renewed efforts.)

Two ten-year-olds were using identical unit squares to make shapes and were investigating the perimeters. Using two squares they discovered that the largest perimeter was 8 units and the smallest 6. "How could you obtain a perimeter of 7 units?" asked the teacher. The boys moved the

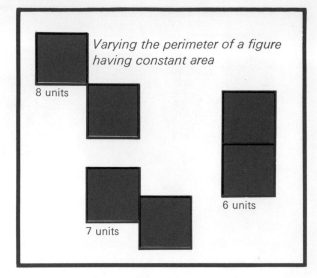

Varying the perimeter of a figure having constant area

8 units

6 units

7 units

squares into the third position. As they did so, they estimated $6\frac{1}{4}$, $6\frac{1}{2}$, $6\frac{3}{4}$, 7. One boy said: "We could make every perimeter between 6 and 8." He appreciated that there were upper and lower limits in this problem.

A class of 10- and 11-year-olds had cut out and mounted the sequence of rectangles with area 36 square inches: $\frac{1}{2}$" by 72", 1" by 36", 2" by 18", 3" by 12", 4" by 9", 6" by 6". The teacher asked them what the length of a rectangle $\frac{1}{4}$" wide would be. A girl replied: "144 inches or 4 yards, and the next will be $1/8$" by 8 yards, $1/16$" by 16 yards and so on until the rectangle is thin as a piece of paper — and very, very long. It will never quite disappear," she added. This girl had a very clear idea of a mathematical limit. So, too, had the bright ten-year-olds who continued their investigations of angles of polygons of increasing number of sides (page 152) to 450 million. "When we saw the pattern we realized that we never should reach 180° or turn the graph," they wrote.

8-8. Graphs and Algebra

Many examples of graphs have been given in the preceding pages. Students enjoy making pictorial representations of various kinds and use these freely to solve problems and to obtain fresh information which may suggest a new investigation. But at some stage the accumulated and

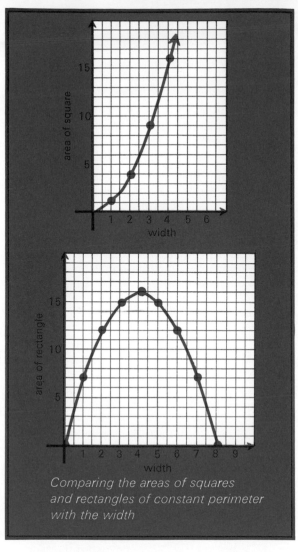

*Comparing the areas of squares
and rectangles of constant perimeter
with the width*

Negative Numbers

Once students are familiar with the number line
this can be extended to include the numerals for
the negative integers with the *negative numerals* in
a different colour to avoid using signs. Wait for
students to ask questions.

An 8-year-old boy sat looking intently at the
extension of the number line his teacher had
recently added. Suddenly he jumped up saying:
"I can subtract with those numbers over there,
too." This was the time for the teacher to introduce
the new numbers formally.

Some ten-year-olds had drawn the graph of the
area of squares and of the area of rectangles with
constant perimeter. From the two tables of values
they discovered that the differences between
successive areas for each gave an odd number
pattern. When they compared the two graphs they
asked: "Where is the other half of the squares
graph?" "Count backwards and see," said the
teacher. The students were quick to see that while
you could not have a square with a side of $^-2$,
you could solve $y = x^2$ for $x = {}^-2$. (See graphs to
the left.)

Graphs

Some ten-year-olds first represented the multiplication tables, using cubes in different colours.
They noticed the equal steps of the staircases they
made. Then they decided to make column graphs
of the tables. The 2-times table is represented in
the graph (including 2 times zero). The students
were surprised to find that the tops of the columns
were in a straight line. They drew this in — and then
established that the intervening fractional values
of x could be doubled by using the line — and that
fractional values of y could be halved by reading
the corresponding values for x. They were discovering that in a relationship graph every point on
the line belongs to the relationship (the justification
for drawing the line).[†] When the teacher asked his
pupils what the relationship between the x values
and the y values was for the 2-times table, they
replied at once: "y is always twice x" and eventually wrote $y = 2x$.

[†]A teacher must be careful that students do not get the impression that
only line graphs represent relations.

varied knowledge which students have gained by
this means needs to be systematized. Normally the
secondary school will be the place for this, but
students with outstanding enthusiasm for more
abstract mathematics may well begin to system-
atize for themselves.

At the elementary level, graphical relationships
form a good introduction to algebra. Students will
be discovering relationships as they look for
patterns in their tables of values. If they are encouraged to find the "n^{th}" term, whenever they
discover a pattern, they will gradually acquire
facility with algebraic expressions.

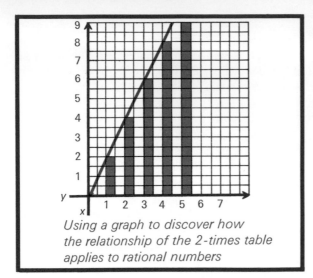

*Using a graph to discover how
the relationship of the 2-times table
applies to rational numbers*

A further discussion of this will be found in Chapter 9. Chapter 9 is intended as a background chapter for elementary teachers — and for further classroom topics for secondary teachers.

8-9. Sets and Relations

The past few years have seen an often hasty attempt to introduce sets into elementary schools with insufficient in-service or pre-service preparation of teachers and with little or no attempt to change classroom methods. In many cases this movement has only resulted in a change from teaching students one type of technique to that of teaching a less familiar type of technique, perhaps imperfectly known and little understood. Since the purpose of our text is to encourage teachers to give students experiences with real materials that with help them to better understand mathematical ideas, we are deliberately not using the word set in its strictest mathematical sense.

We agree that the attention which the new idea of sets has focussed on the structure of mathematics, including arithmetic, is good. It is therefore important that all teachers should know as much about the idea of sets as they can. It is useful to use the word *set* when referring to collections. Children have varied experience in sorting and classifying sets. Every time they sort the elements of a set they are dividing the set into subsets. Subsets must be clearly defined; i.e., the set of red beads in this box.

Operations on sets often present difficulties for pupils, as the following example shows.

Some pupils had been on an expedition and had brought back flower and leaf collections. The teacher suggested that each should put his collection on a large sheet of paper (to define the set) and should then use coloured loops of string to sort his collection as he pleased. One boy used a red loop to contain all the pink flowers. Then he decided to sort the 5-petalled flowers. He first took a loop and enclosed all the 5-petalled flowers which were not pink. Then he found that some of the pink flowers had 5 petals. After some thought he moved the loop containing the 5-petalled flowers until it touched the loop containing the set of pink flowers. He placed the pink flowers with 5 petals near the edge of the red loop, as near to the set of 5-petalled flowers as possible. But he did not think of overlapping the loops!

Students often find the idea of an object having two characteristics at once (pink and five-petalled) difficult. You should let them reach the stage of overlapping the loops themselves. Your pupils will not come to any harm if you decide to leave operations on sets to the secondary school. There is no reason, however, why you should not experiment with these ideas if you are interested.

Relations

Much of the experience provided for your students will be simple experience in relations. The abstract ideas of relations should be postponed to the secondary school. Many of the relations students meet at the elementary level will be ordering relations. One of the difficulties that elementary children encounter is illustrated in the following example:

Three seven-year-old children, Adrian, Martin and Margaret were comparing their heights. First they drew around themselves and painted lifesize portraits. However, it was not easy to compare their heights this way so they cut wide strips of paper to match each height. They mounted these on paper and wrote: "Adrian is tallest. Martin is shortest. Margaret is in the middle." Encouraged by the teacher they then said: "Adrian is taller than Martin and Margaret. Martin is shorter than Margaret and Adrian." But they found it difficult to describe Margaret because she was both shorter than Adrian and taller than Martin. They then found a girl, Ann, and a boy, Graham, who were the same height as Adrian.

Main types of relationships

Equations	Graphs	Classroom Activities
Cubes $y = x^3$		volume and diameter of balls, volume and edge of cubes, and of other similar objects.
Squares $y = x^2$		area and side of squares, area and side of regular triangles, area and radius of circles.
Straight lines $y = x$		perimeter and side of squares and regular triangles. circumference and radius of circles.
Constant product $xy = 1$ or $y = 1/x$ $(x \neq 0)$		relationship between width and length of rectangles of constant area, between the angle at the centre of a regular polygon and its number of sides, between pairs of numbers forming a constant product in the multiplication table.

Two types of relations are illustrated by this example: an ordering relation and an equivalence relation. We can ask pupils simple questions such as, "Adrian is taller than Margaret. Would this statement be true if we reversed the names? Graham is the same height as Adrian. Would this statement be true if we reversed the names? Graham is the same height as Ann who is the same height as Adrian. Is Graham the same height as Adrian? Adrian is taller than Margaret who is taller than Martin. Is Adrian taller than Martin?"

The relations presented at this level are easy for children to identify; however, the systematization of relations is difficult and should be postponed until secondary school.

Chapter 9

Mathematics for the Teacher

9-1	Arithmetic	166
9-2	Sets and Operations on Sets	167
9-3	Algebra	169
9-4	Geometry	173
9-5	Limits	177
9-6	Graph Sets	179
9-7	Groups	179
9-8	Equalities and Inequalities	181
9-9	Statistics	183

Mathematics — What is it? It is interesting to ask this question before a workshop or course begins and to compare the initial answers with those given at the end.

How many of us intuitively recognize mathematics in our surroundings — in the patterns of the textiles we wear — dresses, ties, scarves? Mathematics is not confined to pop art! Most of us are aware of mathematics in the highly mechanized world in which we live: cranes, bridges, building structures and space rockets. We are also aware of mathematics in our homes: furniture, floor tiling, electrical mixers and washing machines. But are we as conscious of the mathematical basis and of the mathematical possibilities of the natural world: the symmetries of flowers and leaves, the polygons formed when mud dries and cracks, the many spirals in nature: sea shells, climbing plants, the arrangement of sunflower seeds in the flower head? Even the spirals in metals can be seen under a microscope.

Earlier in this book we wrote: "Mathematics is a search for relationships in the environment." We can now add: "Mathematics is concerned with the patterns and relationships in the natural and man-made environment." In this respect mathematics resembles science; indeed it is often difficult to distinguish between these two subjects. Both subjects help us to understand and to come to terms with our environment. Where, then, do the two subjects part company? Science is

normally concerned with problems of the real environment and results in experiments with real objects or materials to verify theories; mathematics, "Queen and servant of science," is often concerned with abstractions for which no real materials are required. In order to be able to make these abstractions, most children, to begin with, need firsthand experience with materials. Archimedes, one of the greatest mathematicians and scientists of all time, described his method of finding areas of some unusual shapes: "In mathematics, when I am faced with a new problem, in imagination I weigh and measure." So Archimedes, too, had to draw on previous experience to solve some of the problems he set himself. Therefore, in order to develop in students the mathematical imagination they require to be able to solve textbook problems we must provide them with real experience.

Professor Polya, of Stanford University, a world figure in the teaching of mathematics, wrote: "Abstractions are important; use all means to make them more tangible. Nothing is too good or too bad, too poetical or too trivial to clarify your abstractions." But it is important, of course, to understand these abstractions ourselves.

9-1. Arithmetic

The first experiences children encounter in arithmetic are matching experiences. Experiences of matching sets of objects precede counting. Setting a table for a meal, giving one paint brush to each child, are natural experiences of matching in which the language of inequality usually precedes that of equality. Counting is itself a matching experience in which each object counted is matched with a corresponding number name.

Natural Numbers

The natural or counting numbers can be generated by addition: 1, 1 + 1, 1 + 1 + 1, 1 + 1 + 1 + 1, etc. There are two aspects of natural numbers. The first is the *cardinal* aspect used for counting objects. When we say there are 5 objects we are using the cardinal aspect. The second is the *ordinal* or ordering aspect. The position of the number on the number line determines this ordinal aspect; 5 comes after 4 and before 6. It is the fifth natural number.

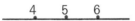

Although our number system is man-made, it has evolved in such a way that the numbers behave in an orderly manner. (However, few children think so when they are compelled to learn number facts without understanding them.)

Extension of the Number System

The order of adding or multiplying a pair of the natural numbers is immaterial and the answer obtained is always one of the set of natural numbers.

If you try to commute in subtraction you no longer obtain the same result, e.g. 5 − 2 = 3
2 − 5 = ?
The answer to 2 − 5 is no longer one of the set of natural numbers. In order to obtain an answer, the number line has to be extended to include the negative integers and zero.

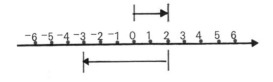

When this is done you can find an answer to 2 − 5, ⁻3 (negative 3). When thinking of the position of a number on the extended number line it is a help to write the negative integers ⁻5, etc. and the positive integers ⁺5, with the signs raised to distinguish the notation for integers from that for the operations of subtraction and addition. Further reference to this notation will be found in the algebra section.

Also, when you try to commute in division you no longer obtain the same result. 8 ÷ 4 = 2
4 ÷ 8 = ?
The answer to 4 ÷ 8 is not a member of the set of natural numbers. The number which multiplied by 8 gives 4 is ½ since there are 8 halves in 4. We must extend the number system to include the fractions (each of which is the ratio of two integers) or rational numbers. These too, can be given a place on the number line.

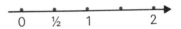

Fractions

In Chapter 7 we showed some types of experiences which will lead children to invent their own methods of performing operations on fractions. Children should never be taught tricks to accomplish the operations on fractions.

Equivalence of fractions is of vital importance: $^1/_2 = {}^2/_4 = {}^3/_6 = {}^4/_8$ etc. When a child discovers this by a variety of practical methods it may well be one of his first experiences with an infinite set. It should be an exciting experience. Once he knows this, he can devise his own methods of adding, subtracting, multiplying and dividing fractions. The fractions used should be simple and realistic.

The written notation we use to express fractions is not easy for children as this is the first time they will meet a pair of numbers to write what may seem to them to be one object: three-quarters of a piece of ribbon. Fractions are in fact ordered number pairs. $^3/_4$ is very different from $^4/_3$. The English names of the fractions are often easier for children than the written mathematical notation (half is easier than $^1/_2$).

Decimals

Decimals or decimal fractions are another extension of our number notation. Children have early experience of the use of decimals in using money – many know that there are ten cents in a dime, ten dimes in a dollar – and so have already used decimals before they meet the written notation.

100	10	1	$^1/_{10}$	$^1/_{100}$
3	5	2	5	0

or 352.50.

The operations of addition, subtraction, multiplication and division should not present any difficulty to children if the number system is understood and if these operations have already been devised by children for the natural numbers.

Basic Laws for the Set of Rational Numbers

The basic rules or laws that determine this orderly behaviour should be known and understood by teachers. These laws are commutative, associative, distributive, identity and inverse.

The commutative laws of addition and multiplication for any rational numbers a and b are $a + b = b + a$ and $a \times b = b \times a$.

The *order* of performing addition or multiplication on two or more rational numbers is immaterial – the result is the same.

The associative laws of addition and multiplication for any rational numbers a, b and c are $a + (b + c) = (a + b) + c$ and $a \times (b \times c) = (a \times b) \times c$.

The *grouping* of addition or of multiplication is immaterial.

The distributive law of multiplication over addition is $a (b + c) = ab + ac$

We use this in long multiplication:
$$26 \times 54 = 26 (50 + 4)$$
$$= (26 \times 50) + (26 \times 4)$$
$$= 1300 + 104$$
$$= 1404$$

Identity elements for addition and multiplication are 0 and 1 respectively.
The additive identity is sometimes called the zero element; adding it to a number leaves the number unchanged. $a + 0 = a$

The multiplicative identity is sometimes called the unity element; multiplying it by a number leaves the number unchanged. $a \times 1 = a$

Inverse elements for addition and multiplication are ^-a and $\frac{1}{a}$. Adding any number to its inverse results in zero. $a + {^-a} = 0$

Multiplying any number by its reciprocal (except zero) results in one. $a \times \frac{1}{a} = 1$

9-2. Sets and Operations on Sets

The word *set* is useful when referring to collections of objects and may be introduced at whatever level you teach. As soon as you begin to sort the elements (objects) of a set you are dividing the set into subsets. It is always important to define clearly the set of elements you are considering: the universal set.

Intersection of Sets

Let the universal set, E, be the set of whole numbers 1 to 16 inclusive.
$$A = \{4, 8, 12, 16\}$$
$$B = \{1, 4, 9, 16\}$$
In this example elements 4 and 16 are common to both set A and to set B. This new set represented by the shaded region of fig. 2 is called the *intersection* of A and B. The intersection set of two sets contains only the elements common to both. In many textbooks you will find this written $A \cap B$.

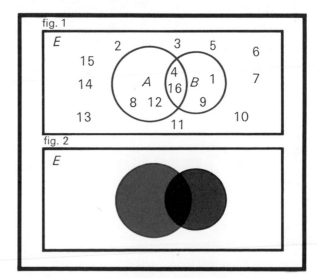

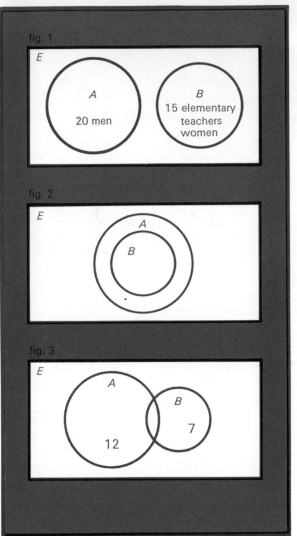

fig. 1

E

A
20 men

B
15 elementary
teachers
women

fig. 2

E

A
B

fig. 3

E

A
B

12
7

The Union of Sets

At a teachers' workshop 15 of the teachers worked in elementary schools and 20 of the teachers were men. Set E (the universal set) is the set of all teachers attending the workshop. Set A is the set of 20 men. Set B is the set of 15 elementary teachers. How many teachers are there altogether? Can we be sure? How many possibilities are there altogether? The solution of this problem involves the second way of combining sets: the *union* of sets.

If the 15 elementary teachers are all women, sets A and B are said to be disjoint sets and the number of teachers in set $E = 35$ (the addition of two disjoint sets with 20 and 15 elements respectively).

If the 15 elementary teachers are all men, B is a subset of A and the number of teachers in set $E = 20$.

If some of the elementary teachers are men (in the diagram 8 elementary teachers are men), the number of teachers in set E is the number common to both sets and the remaining members in sets A and B, in this case 27. How many other variations of this pattern are there?

In many texts the union is written $A \cup B$. Caution must be exercised not to introduce the ideas of intersection and union too early to young children. The following is a brief summary for reference; however, this knowledge is not essential. There are three different possibilities. Suppose the universal set is the set of natural numbers between 20 and 40:

a/ The sets have some elements in common:
Set A is the set of even numbers
$$A = \{22, 24, 26, 28, 30, 32, 34, 36, 38\}$$
Set B is the set of squares of numbers
$$B = \{25, 36\}$$
The intersection of sets A and B is $\{36\}$.
The union of sets A and B
is $\{22, 24, 25, 26, 28, 30, 32, 34, 36, 38\}$. There is no need to put these in order, of course!

b/ One set is entirely contained in the other:
set A is the set of even numbers
set C is the multiples of 4
$$A = \{22, 24, 26, 28, 30, 32, 34, 36, 38\}$$
$$C = \{24, 28, 32, 36\}$$
$$A \cap C = \{24, 28, 32, 36\}$$
$$A \cup C = \{22, 24, 26, 28, 30, 32, 34, 36, 38\}$$

c/ The sets are distinct — called disjoint — and have no elements in common:
set A is the set of even numbers
$$A = \{22, 24, 26, 28, 30, 32, 34, 36, 38\}$$
set D is the set of odd numbers
$$D = \{21, 23, 25, 27, 29, 31, 33, 35, 37, 39\}$$
$A \cap D = \{\ \}$ (the empty set or null set)
$A \cup D = \{21, 22, 23, 24, 25, 26, 27, 28, 29, 30, 31,$
$\quad 32, 33, 34, 35, 36, 37, 38, 39\}$
Addition is often defined in terms of the union of disjoint sets. Can you explain why?

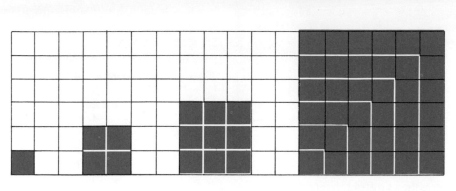

A sequence of overlapped squares

9-3. Algebra

It would be impossible to consider all of the important topics of algebra in a text of this kind. However, we have singled out certain topics that lend themselves to the active learning approach. Experiences that we provide children greatly enhance the probability that our students will be able to learn and understand algebra.

Exponents

These have already been met in arithmetic in our number system and in arithmetic in other bases. Compare the following:

1000	10^3	8	2^3	a^3	a^3
100	10^2	4	2^2	a^2	a^2
10	10^1	2	2^1	a	a^1
1	10^0	1	2^0	1	a^0
$1/10$ or .1	10^{-1}	½	2^{-1}	$1/a$	a^{-1}
$1/100$ or .01	10^{-2}	¼	2^{-2}	$1/a^2$	a^{-2}
		⅛	2^{-3}		

You will see how maintenance of the pattern in the left and right hand columns shows that 1 must be written as 10^0, 2^0, a^0, etc.

A second reason for calling $a^0 = 1$ is that this definition allows the rules for operations with non-negative exponents to hold for operations with both negative and non-negative exponents.

$2^2 \cdot 2^3 = 2^5$	$2^3 \cdot 2^{-1} = 2^2$
$4 \cdot 8 = 32$	$8 \cdot ½ = 4$
$2^1 \cdot 2^{-1} = 2^0$	$2^{-1} \cdot 2^{-2} = 2^{-3}$
$2 \cdot ½ = 1$	$½ \cdot ¼ = ⅛$

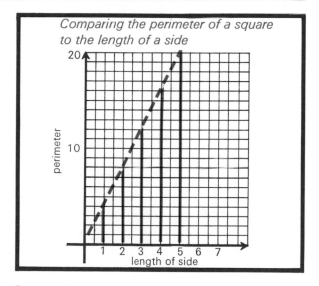

Comparing the perimeter of a square to the length of a side

Sequences

Many sequences can be developed in the work on shapes — for example, sequences showing how squares grow as their sides are increased by 1 (this can be done with unit squares or on 1″ graph paper). Sequences of successive perimeters (P) and areas (A) for successive sides (S) are shown in the table.

S ins.	0	1	2	3	4	5	...	n	$n+1$
P ins.	0	4	8	12	16	20	...	$4n$	$4(n+1)$
A sq. ins.	0	1	4	9	16	25	...	n^2	$(n+1)^2$

We have included zero, the nth, and $(n+1)^{th}$ terms of these sequences in the table.

Successive differences for the perimeter sequence are constant: 4. If the sequence is represented as a block or column graph this will show clearly. Test to see whether the tops of the columns are in a straight line. Successive differences for the area sequence are:

$1,3,5,7,9,\ldots,(n+1)^2 - n^2$

[note $(n+1)^2 - n^2 = n^2 + 2n - 1 - n^2 = 2n - 1$]

Successive differences are no longer equal but form a new sequence: that of odd numbers. When successive points in the area sequence are graphed they will not be in a straight line. These are marked with dots on the graph. (The differences of the odd numbers in this sequence are, of course, equal.)

Build a sequence of cubes with unit cubes. Successive volumes (V) for corresponding edges (S) are:

S ins.	0	1	2	3	4	5	...	$n-1$	n	$n+1$
V cu. ins.	0	1	8	27	64	125	...	$(n-1)^3$	n^3	$(n+1)^3$

(inch cubes)

1st differences		1		7		19		37		61
2nd differences			6		12		18		24	
3rd differences				6		6		6		

Since $(n-1)^3 = n^3 - 3n^2 + 3n - 1$ and
$(n+1)^3 = n^3 + 3n^2 + 3n + 1$,
the successive differences of the
$(n-1)^{th}, n^{th}$, and $(n+1)^{th}$ terms
are as follows:

1st D $3n^2 - 3n + 1$ $3n^2 + 3n + 1$

2nd D $6n$

(or sequence 6, 12, 18, etc. with difference 6)

Operations on the positive and negative integers

It is easier, at least in the beginning, to use raised signs to indicate the positive and negative integers to distinguish these *directional* signs from the signs for the operations of addition and subtraction.

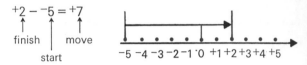

It is especially important to use these raised signs when marking positive and negative integers on a number line. Students who have had experience in adding and subtracting the positive integers on a number line do not find it difficult to extend these operations to include the negative integers; indeed, they sometimes do this spontaneously for themselves. For this purpose the operation of addition may be interpreted as the answer to the question: Starting at $+2$, what is the final position of a movement of -5?

$+2 + {}^-5 = {}^-3$

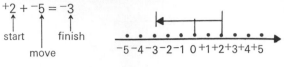

Subtraction is the inverse of addition and the question is now: Starting at -5, what must I add to get a final position of $+2$?
or How far is it from -5 to $+2$?

$+2 - {}^-5 = {}^+7$

Multiplication, $+2 \times {}^-5$, is the answer to the question: Starting at zero, what is the final position of two movements of -5, that is, two steps of -5?

$+2 \times {}^-5 = {}^-10$

If the commutative law is to hold, then multiplying a positive number by a negative number must be the same as multiplying the negative number by the positive number.

${}^-3 \times {}^+4 = {}^+4 \times {}^-3 = {}^-12$

Multiplication of integers can also be explained by continuing a pattern:

$+2 \times {}^+4 = {}^+8$
$+1 \times {}^+4 = {}^+4$
$0 \times {}^+4 = 0$
$-1 \times {}^+4 = {}^-4$
$-2 \times {}^+4 = {}^-8$

    The pattern is formed by repeated subtraction of 4.

$+2 \times {}^-5 = {}^-10$
$+1 \times {}^-5 = {}^-5$
$0 \times {}^-5 = 0$
$-1 \times {}^-5 = {}^+5$
$-2 \times {}^-5 = {}^+10$

    The pattern is formed by repeated addition of 5.

Division is the inverse of multiplication.

$+3 \times {}^+4 = {}^+12$ so $+12 \div {}^+3 = {}^+4$
$+3 \times {}^-4 = {}^-12$ so $-12 \div {}^-4 = {}^+3$
                     and $-12 \div {}^+3 = {}^-4$
$-4 \times {}^-3 = {}^+12$ so $+12 \div {}^-3 = {}^-4$

Mathematical sentences and equations†

$3 + n = 7$ is an open sentence; it is a true statement when the variable $n = 4$. It is false for all other values!

$3 + n < 7$ If the solution is restricted to natural numbers this open sentence is true for $n = 1, 2, 3$.

$3 + n > 7$ If the solution is restricted to natural numbers this open sentence is true for $n = 5, 6, 7, \ldots$; that is, for all the natural numbers greater than 4.

Some sentences are true for only one value of the variable

$$\Box + \Box + \Box = 12 \qquad \Box = 4$$

others for many values

$$\Box \times 1 = \Box$$
$$\Box + 0 = \Box$$

In most of the work in algebra that we will present in this chapter, we will consider only possible integral values. We are interested here in presenting teachers with possible activities for their pupils. In order for pupils to use active learning in these algebraic topics, we must give them the opportunity to discover relationships by trying out different values. For this reason we are limiting ourselves for the most part to integral values.

The value or values of the variable which make an open sentence true are not always obvious, but can usually be found.

$5 + 2n = 11$

n	$5 + 2n$	True/False
2	9	False – too small
4	13	False – too large
3	11	True

$6n - 5 = 50$

n	$6n - 5$	True/False
8	43	too small
9	49	too small
10	55	too large
9.1	49.6	too small
9.2	50.2	too large

9.2 may be regarded as the best approximation at this stage.

†A thorough treatment of this topic will be found in *Discovery in Mathematics* and *Explorations in Mathematics*, by Robert Davis. (See section 3-4.)

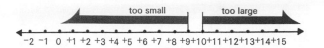

too small   too large

Two variables are commonly found in many mathematical sentences or equations.

$\Box + \triangle = 6$ or $x + y = 6$

x	0	1	2	6
y	6	5	4	0

Children do not normally make a systematic table in the first instance but suggest, for example, one ordered pair of numbers which satisfy this relationship (4,2). When the table is complete, the pattern can be extended. The negative integers are then included: $(7, ^-1)$, $(8, ^-2)$, also $(^-1, 7)$. The extension to include negative integers will be better understood when these number pairs are plotted on a graph.

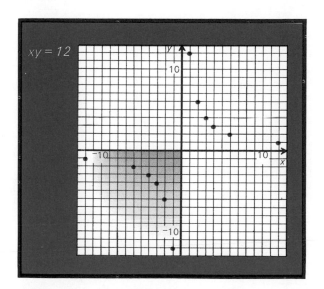

$\Box \times \triangle = 12$ or $xy = 12$

x	1	2	3	4	6	12
y	12	6	4	3	2	1

Here, although part of the pattern is easy to see, it may not be so easy to continue this to include the negative integers. The graph does not help as in the first example because the ordered pairs are now $(^-1, ^-12)$, $(^-2, ^-6)$, and these points all appear in the third (shaded) quadrant of the plane.

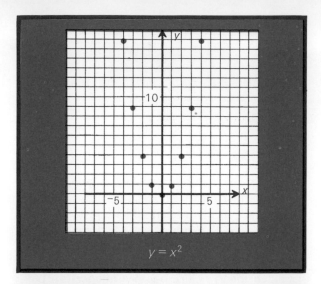

$y = x^2$

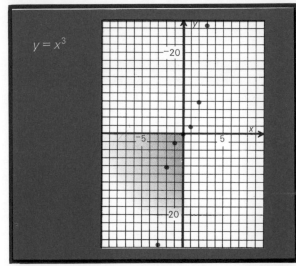

$y = x^3$

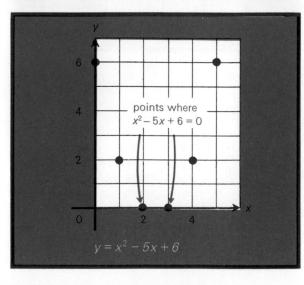

points where
$x^2 - 5x + 6 = 0$

$y = x^2 - 5x + 6$

$\triangle = \square \times \square$ or $y = x^2$

x	0	1	2	3	4
y	0	1	4	9	16

In this equation both positive and negative integers are possible for the variable x.

If the pattern is extended to include the negative integers the ordered pairs are $(^-1, ^+1)$, $(^-2, ^+4)$, $(^-3, ^+9)$. It is interesting to compare this with the next example.

$\triangle = \square \times \square \times \square$ or $y = x^3$

x	0	1	2	3	4
y	0	1	8	27	64

Here, too, both positive and negative integers satisfy this relationship.

If $x = ^-1$, $y = (^-1)^3$
$$= (^-1 \times ^-1) \times ^-1$$
$$= ^+1 \times ^-1$$
$$= ^-1$$

Therefore, if we include negative integers some of the ordered pairs are $(^-1, ^-1)$, $(^-2, ^-8)$, $(^-3, ^-27)$, and on the graph these appear in the third quadrant (shaded).

Equations

Linear equations (one solution only) have been introduced and solved by trial and error earlier in this text.

$3 + n = 7$	$5 + 2n = 11$
$3n = 12$	$6n - 5 = 50$

Equations with more than one solution may also, in the first instance, be solved by trial and error.

$\square \times \square - 5\square + 6 = 0$ or $x^2 - 5x + 6 = 0$

The two values of the variable which satisfy this equation are 2 and 3.

x	Result	Comment
1	2	too large
2	0	true
3	0	true

Look at the graph of $y = x^2 - 5x + 6$ and find the values of x when $y = 0$; you will understand why there are only two values of the variable which satisfy the equation $x^2 - 5x + 6 = 0$.

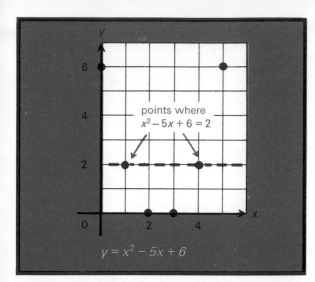

points where
$x^2 - 5x + 6 = 2$

$y = x^2 - 5x + 6$

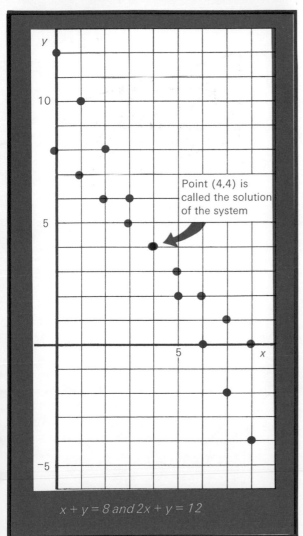

Point (4,4) is
called the solution
of the system

$x + y = 8$ and $2x + y = 12$

The same graph may also be used to solve equations such as $x^2 - 5x + 6 = 2$ (where y equals constants other than 0).

Systems of equations may also be solved by experimentation.

$x + y = 8$		$2x + y = 12$	
x	y	x	y
0	8	0	12
1	7	1	10
2	6	2	8
3	5	3	6
4	4	4	4
5	3	5	2
6	2	6	0
7	1	7	$^-2$
8	0	8	$^-4$

9-4. Geometry

Whether a teacher structures the classroom environment carefully or allows more freedom for pupils to develop their own interests, there are certain aspects of shape which are sure to arise. It is therefore important that teachers themselves should know the mathematical background of these topics in order to be able to develop them to the limit of the children's capacities.

In this section we have therefore considered the properties of various three-dimensional and two-dimensional shapes, particularly cubes, cylinders, cones and regular polygons; symmetry and congruence; mathematical similarity and enlargement, and limits (with special reference to shapes).

Properties of Familiar Shapes

Two-dimensional shapes such as circles, rectangles, squares, diamonds (rhombuses) and triangles are normally recognized after a child can sort three-dimensional shapes. Examples of children's work in the last chapter illustrated some of the difficulties children experience in this field.

Interesting experiments can be carried out to find the volumes of a set of cylinders of equal diameters and different heights or a set of cylinders of equal heights and different diameters.

$V_{cylinder} =$ base area × height $= \pi r^2 h$

When the base areas are the same (diameters equal), πr^2 is constant; therefore, $V = ah$. The relationship is a linear one and the graph will be a straight line. When the heights are the same πh is a constant; $V = br^2$. This relationship is comparable with the curve $y = x^2$. The experiment can be repeated with sets of cones. It is then possible to find the relationship of the volume of a cone to the volume of a cylinder of the same diameter and height ($\frac{1}{3}$ volume of a cylinder = volume of a cone = $\frac{1}{3}\pi r^2 h$).

To find the area of the curved surface of a cone, the relationships between the radius of the base, r, the height, h, and the slant height, s, must be considered. The area of the curved surface of the cone is some fractional part, $^9/_{12}$, $^{21}/_{24}$, etc.

Polygons

The following Venn diagram will help classify the parallelogram family of quadrilaterals.

Set Q, the set of quadrilaterals
Set P, the set of parallelograms
Set E, the set of rhombuses
Set R, the set of rectangles
Set S, the set of squares

All parallelograms are quadrilaterals.
All rhombuses and all rectangles are parallelograms. The intersection of set R with set E is the set of squares; that is, squares are both rectangles and rhombuses.

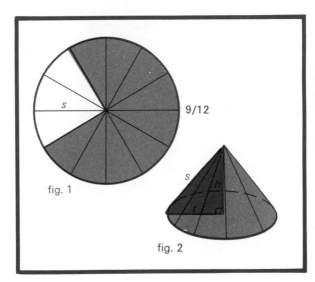

fig. 1

9/12

fig. 2

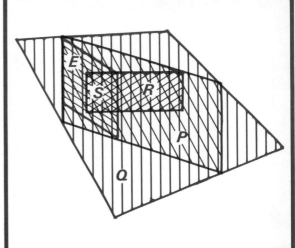

of the area of a generating circle whose radius is the slant height, s. When a cone is formed a smaller circular base is obtained. Thus the fraction can be found from the ratio of the circumference of the base circle to that of the generating circle.

$$\frac{\text{Circumference of base circle}}{\text{Circumference of generating circle}} = \frac{2\pi r}{2\pi s} = \frac{r}{s}$$

Area of curved surface $= \dfrac{r}{s}(\pi s^2)$

Note that the radius, height and slant height are related by the Pythagorean theorem.
$$r^2 + h^2 = s^2$$

If a graph of (r, h) is drawn a quadrant of a circle is obtained.

The sequence of rigid regular polygons obtained by successively adding strips from one vertex to the others in a sequence of regular frames is shown in the figure below and the chart at the top of the next page.

Number of vertices or sides	(1) Number of strips	(2) Number of triangles	(3) Angle Sum of polygon in right angles	(4) Interior angle of polygon in degrees	(5) Exterior angle of polygon
3	0	1	2	$\dfrac{180°}{3}$ 60°	120°
4	1	2	4	$\dfrac{360°}{4}$ 90°	90°
5	2	3	6	$\dfrac{540°}{5}$ 108°	72°
6	3	4	8	$\dfrac{720°}{6}$ 120°	60°
n	$n-3$	$n-2$	$2(n-2)$ or $2n-4$	$\dfrac{2n-4}{n}$ (90°)	$\dfrac{4}{n}$ (90°)

If n denotes the number of sides, then the number of strips, (1), is $n-3$;
number of triangles, (2), is $n-2$;
sum of polygon angles, (3), is $2(n-2)$ or $2n-4$;
interior angle, (4), is $\dfrac{2n-4}{n}$ or $2-\dfrac{4}{n}$ right angles;
exterior angle, (5), is $2-(2-\dfrac{4}{n})$ or $\dfrac{4}{n}$ right angles.

(1), (2) and (3) are found to be linear relationships. It is interesting to speculate about what happens next in (2) and (3). It is easier to plot (4) interior angles of regular 3, 4, 5, . . . sided polygons in degrees. It is interesting to plot this graph when the number of sides is 360 (179°), 3600 (179.9°), etc. You can see what is happening as the number of sides gets greater.

It is also interesting to plot the interior and exterior angles on the same axes so that the symmetry can be seen. You will note that these graphs are not drawn continuous. However, a dotted line has been put in to indicate that there is a continuous relationship. The relationship between the angle at the centre of a regular polygon and its number of sides is $y=\dfrac{360}{n}$.

This is the same as the relationship between the exterior angle of a regular polygon and its number of sides (5). The sum of the exterior angles of any polygon is, surprisingly, 4 right angles.

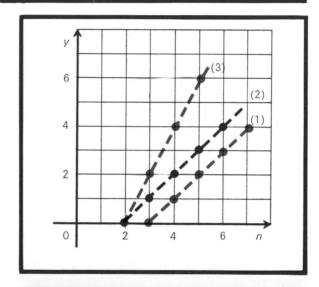

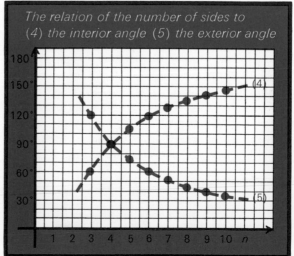

The relation of the number of sides to (4) the interior angle (5) the exterior angle

Edge (ins.)	Total "perimeter"	Number of cubes (Volume V)	Skin or surface area A (sq. ins.)	Rate of surface area to A Volume V
0	0	0	0	?
1	12	1	6	6
2	24	8	24	3
3	36	27	54	2
4	48	64	96	1.5
5	60	125	150	1.2
6	72	216	216	1

Symmetry and Congruence

Many classroom activities, including art and craft, provide opportunities for the exploration of symmetrical shapes. Small rectangular mirrors made to stand upright by means of a small base fastened at the back are invaluable for this purpose. The graph of the relationship between the angle formed by two hinged mirrors and the number of images seen, including the object, is a difficult one – since it is a discontinuous graph. 4 images (3 reflections and 1 object) are seen as soon as the angle between the mirrors is less than 120°. 4 images continue to be visible until this angle is 90°. As soon as the angle is less than 90° a fifth image comes into view. This problem is also worth studying when a line joining 2 points, one on each mirror, equidistant from the hinge, is used as the object.

Congruence can be associated with attractive textile patterns on dresses, drapes, and even neckties. Floor tiling and attractive repeating patterns in architecture and engineering show congruence in three dimensions as well as two.

Repeating patterns of congruent triangles in 3 colours can be very attractive and can lead to the discovery of the angle sum of a triangle and to the properties of angles made by parallel lines.

Similarity and Enlargement

Similarity has a precise meaning in mathematics: it refers to sets of objects which are identical in shape but of different sizes. (Congruence is therefore a special case of similarity in which objects are of the same shape and size; i.e., are geometrically identical.) Although it may seem to be easier to begin with two-dimensional similar shapes, it is advisable to begin with three dimensions. The easiest example is the cube. In studying a set of cubes the variables are number of edges, total perimeter, volume and surface area. This data for unit cubes is shown in the table above.

Since the surface area of a unit cube of edge x is $6x^2$ and its volume is x^3, the A/V ratio in general is

$$\frac{6x^2}{x^3} = \frac{6}{x}.$$

As the table is continued the A/V ratio will come closer to zero.

The graph of $\frac{A}{V}$, $y = \frac{6x^2}{x^3} = \frac{6}{x}$, is shown above.

Frequently teachers plot Area ($6x^2$) against Volume (x^3). This is a complicated relationship.

We have already considered the graph of $y = x^3$. Compare this with the graph of the total surface or skin area, $y = 6x^2$. These can be plotted on the same axes. A characteristic of 3-dimensional similar shapes is that the volume grows in the sequence of cubes while the surface area grows in the sequence of squares.

$(6, 24, 54, 96, \ldots, 6x^2)$
$(1, \ 4, \ 9, 16, \ldots, \ x^3)$

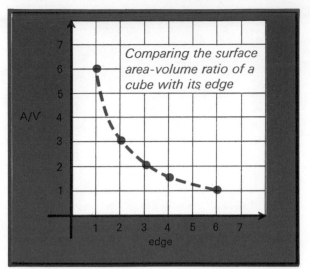

Comparing the surface area-volume ratio of a cube with its edge

A/V

edge

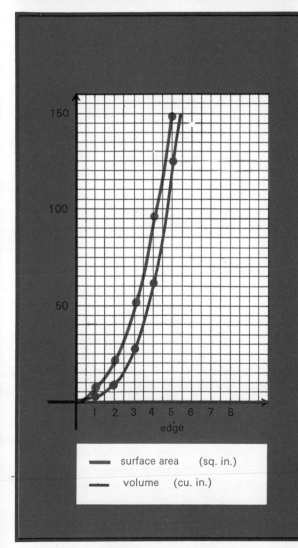

edge

— surface area (sq. in.)

— volume (cu. in.)

It is very important to be able to distinguish among those mathematical shapes which are always similar: cubes, spheres, squares, circles, regular polygons; and those which are similar under certain conditions: rectangles, triangles, ellipses, kites, etc.

9-5. Limits

Here are some simple but important examples of limits involving perimeter, area and volume. Experiment to find the smallest and largest area you can enclose using a 24 inch — ½ inch strip of construction paper. The smallest will be zero. The largest will be a circle with an approximate area of 46 square inches. If you make rectangular shapes the largest area will be a square, 36 square inches. The area of the circle is more than 25% larger than that of the square.

The area of a simple closed curve with a perimeter of 24″ has a lower limit of zero and an upper limit of 46 square inches. The area can, in this case, be zero since "all the area can be squashed out," as a nine-year-old boy said.

The area can be seen to increase as the number of sides of the shapes enclosed increases. This problem in three dimensions is not easy. We have to discover the limits of the volume of shapes made with unit cubes when, for example, the surface area is 144 square inches. If the shapes made are to be confined to cuboids, the problem is simpler — but not easy.

Another interesting limit can be obtained from *the golden section* used so frequently in medieval paintings. The most important part of the picture was seldom centrally placed, but placed at the *golden mean*. The golden mean of a line segment AB is the point X which divides segment AB in the same ratio as the whole segment and the larger part;

$$\frac{AX}{XB} = \frac{AB}{AX}$$

   If $AB = 1$ unit and
     $AX = x$ units,
then $XB = 1 - x$ units which gives

$$\frac{x}{1-x} = \frac{1}{x},$$
$$x^2 = 1 - x$$
or $x^2 + x - 1 = 0$.

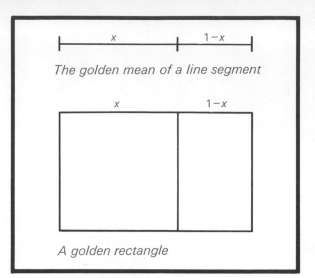

The golden mean of a line segment

A golden rectangle

Using the golden mean, a spiral can be drawn as shown. This has various applications in nature: in fir cones, sunflower heads, shells, etc. The association of the golden mean with a regular pentagon can be seen if you trisect the angle at one of the vertices.

Consider angle A whose measure is 108°; each of its trisected parts has a measure of 36°. Since this is a regular polygon, triangle BAE is isosceles and the measure of its three angles is 180°. Therefore the measure of angle ABE is 36° and BE is a trisector of angle B. By determining the measures of the angles of triangle BAC it can be shown that BAC is also an isosceles triangle with $BA = BC$. (Each part of angle BAE is 36°, since segments

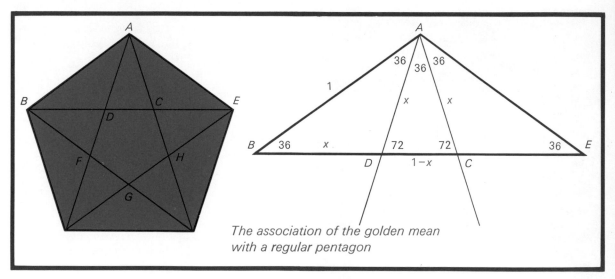

The association of the golden mean
with a regular pentagon

The solutions of this equation are $\dfrac{-1 \pm \sqrt{5}}{2}$.

$\dfrac{-1 + \sqrt{5}}{2}$ is .618 (to 3 decimal places). We need not consider the negative value.

The golden rectangle has sides 1 by x (or .618). Medieval pictures were often of this shape. If the square of side x is removed, the remaining rectangle is another golden rectangle. The ratio of its sides is

$$\frac{x}{1-x} = \frac{1}{x}.$$

If we continue this process of *removing* successive squares from the rectangles we have another example of a limit.

AD and AC belong to the diagonals that trisect angle BAE.)

Suppose each side of the pentagon to be of unit length, then by the "bisector of the angle" theorem (the bisector of the vertical angle divides the base in the ratio of the sides)

$$\frac{BD}{CD} = \frac{BA}{AC} \text{ or } \frac{x}{1-x} = \frac{1}{x}. \text{ Solving for } x, x = .618.$$

In conclusion two diagonals divide each other in golden sections.

The vanishing pentagon (the set of pentagons within pentagons made by the diagonals) is an example comparable with the vanishing triangle and square.[†]

†The film *Donald in Mathmagicland* gives excellent visual experience of this sequence of ideas.

9-6. Graph Sets

Set of Linear Equations

1/ Multiplication tables: $y = 2x$
$$y = 3x$$
2/ Rectangles with constant perimeter:
width + length = 6 or $x + y = 6$.
3/ Perimeters of squares: $y = 4x$
Perimeters of equilateral triangles: $y = 3x$
4/ Circumferences of circles: $y = \pi x$
5/ Interior and exterior angles of polygons:
$x + y = 180$
6/ Weight in air and water of a set of stones
of the same density: $y = ax$
7/ Weight added to spring and stretch of spring:
$y = bx$
8/ Height of bounce of ball and height of drop:
$y = cx$
9/ Weight of pendulum bob and time of swing:
$y = d$ (constant, whatever the weight)

Set of Second Degree Equations

1/ Areas of sets of squares: $y = x^2$
2/ Areas of sets of circles: $y = \pi x^2$
3/ Time of 1 swing and the length of a pendulum:
$T^2 = dl$
4/ Time and distance travelled down the slope
by a truck: $y^2 = dx$
5/ Area of sets of rectangles of constant perimeter:
$x + y = 6$
Area $= xy = x(6 - x)$ or $6x - x^2$

Set of Third Degree Equations

1/ Volume of a set of cubes: $y = x^3$
2/ Volume of a set of balls: $y = {}^4/_3 \pi r^3$
3/ Weight of a set of solid balls of the same
density and their diameters: $W = {}^4/_3 \pi r^3 k$

Set of Constant Product Second Degree Equations

1/ Rectangles of constant area:
$xy = A$ e.g. $xy = 36$
2/ Sum of the angles at the centre of regular
polygons with x number of sides: $xy = 360$
3/ Sum of the exterior angles of regular polygons with x number of sides: $xy = 360$
4/ The relationship of angles between two
hinged mirrors and number of objects and images
seen is a special case. Values at *break points*
belong to $xy = 360$.

9-7. Groups

The brief sections included here are a foretaste
of these important topics. If you are interested or
concerned with the teaching of these topics,
you are recommended to study standard texts.

Vectors

Vectors occur in many branches of mathematics
to represent quantities involving both magnitude
and direction such as velocity, force, and displacement. They may be represented by directed line
segments, or by ordered pairs of numbers which
are the co-ordinates of the terminal point of the
position vector. From a graph find what happens
when you add two vectors $(1, 2)$ followed by
$(5, 1)$. $\overrightarrow{OA} + \overrightarrow{AC}$
What direct displacement would have taken you
to C? $(1, 2) + (5, 1) = (6, 3)$, $\overrightarrow{OC} = (6, 3)$
Another example:
$$\overrightarrow{AB} + \overrightarrow{BC} = (4, 3) + (1, {}^-2) = (5, 1)$$
$$\overrightarrow{AC} = (5, 1)$$
This suggests that we define vector addition as
$\overrightarrow{AB} + \overrightarrow{BC} = \overrightarrow{AC}$.

Since vector addition is associative, commutative and has an identity element and inverse
elements, we say that the set of all vectors in a
plane constitute a commutative group. Below are
some examples illustrating these properties.
$$\overrightarrow{AB} = (1, 4), \overrightarrow{BC} = (2, 3), \overrightarrow{CD} = (1, {}^-2)$$

Associative:
$$\overrightarrow{AB} + (\overrightarrow{BC} + \overrightarrow{CD}) \quad | \quad (\overrightarrow{AB} + \overrightarrow{BC}) + \overrightarrow{CD}$$
$$(1,4) + [(2,3)+(1,{}^-2)] \quad | \quad [(1,4)+(2,3)]+(1,{}^-2)$$
$$(4, 5) = (4, 5)$$

Commutative:
$$\overrightarrow{AB} + \overrightarrow{BC} \quad | \quad \overrightarrow{BC} + \overrightarrow{AB}$$
$$(1, 4) + (2, 3) \quad | \quad (2, 3) + (1, 4)$$
$$(3, 7) = (3, 7)$$

Identity Element:
$$\overrightarrow{DE} = (0, 0)$$
$$\overrightarrow{AB} + \overrightarrow{DE} = \overrightarrow{AB}$$
$$(1, 4) + (0, 0) = (1, 4)$$

Inverse Element:
$$\overrightarrow{EF} = ({}^-1, {}^-4)$$
$$\overrightarrow{AB} + \overrightarrow{EF} = \overrightarrow{DE}$$
$$(1, 4) + ({}^-1, {}^-4) = (0, 0)$$

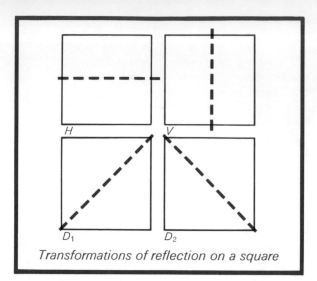

Transformations of reflection on a square

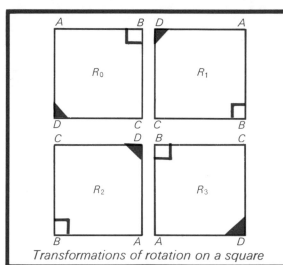

Transformations of rotation on a square

Transformations

The different types of movement or transformation can be performed one after another in a variety of ways. Try the following transformations on a square. (A square is chosen here because it is the most familiar and the simplest of all geometrical shapes.) Label the angles at the vertices of the square 1, 2, 3, 4 in order; the same numerals should appear at each vertex on the front and back surface of the square. Recall that a square has four axes of symmetry. Put an axis of symmetry in each of the four squares. We have called them H (horizontal), V (vertical), D (diagonal). If you reflect the square, in turn, about each of the axes, you will get a new position.

You will also get three new positions if you rotate the square (clockwise) about its centre through 1 right angle (R_1), 2 (R_2) and 3 (R_3) right angles.

No rotation, or rotation through 4, 8, 12 etc. right angles (R_0), will not result in a new position.

The operation considered here is rotation about the centre of the square.

We are going to find the effect of combining 2 of the 4 rotations. Performing these one after the other and entering the results in a table, R_1 followed by R_2 gives R_3. $R_1 * R_2 = R_3$

*	R_0	R_1	R_2	R_3
R_0	R_0	R_1	R_2	R_3
R_1	R_1	R_2	R_3	R_0
R_2	R_2	R_3	R_0	R_1
R_3	R_3	R_0	R_1	R_2

Use this table to answer the following questions:

1/   *Do each two elements of this set combine to form a third which is also an element of the set? (Yes)*

2/   *Does the associative law hold? (Yes)*
$(R_1 * R_2) * R_3 = R_3 * R_3 = ? (R_2)$
$R_1 * (R_2 * R_3) = R_1 * R_1 = ? (R_2)$

3/   *Is there an identity element which leaves the position of the square unchanged? (Yes, R_0)*

4/   *Has each element a unique inverse which combines with it to give the identity element?*
$R_1 * R_3 = ?$ *What is the inverse of R_2? (Yes, R_0, R_2)*

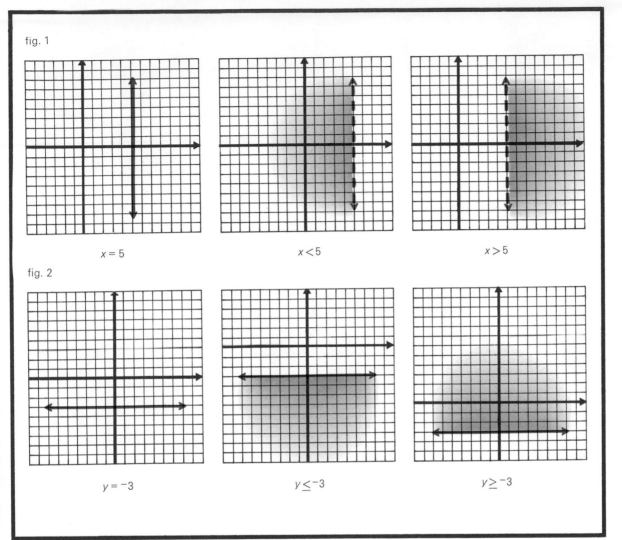

fig. 1

$x = 5$ $x < 5$ $x > 5$

fig. 2

$y = {}^-3$ $y \leq {}^-3$ $y \geq {}^-3$

9-8. Equalities and Inequalities

Children learn the language of inequality: more than, taller than, shorter than, heavier than, lighter than, faster than; before they learn that of equality: as many as, as tall as, as heavy as, or the same weight as. Yet until quite recently the mathematics taught in schools was almost entirely equality. Because of this, many teachers have not had adequate training in the topic of inequality. The mathematics of inequality is part of the real world and is frequently used in business and industry.

Graphs of $x = 5$, $x < 5$, and $x > 5$ are shown in figure 1 and those of $y = {}^-3$, $y \leq {}^-3$ and $y \geq {}^-3$ in figure 2. Some interesting graphs are obtained if we combine two or more inequality statements. (See figures on p. 182.)

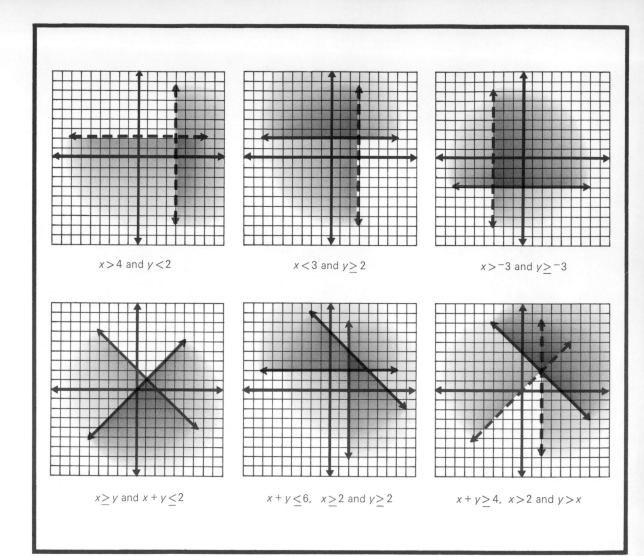

$x > 4$ and $y < 2$

$x < 3$ and $y \geq 2$

$x > {}^-3$ and $y \geq {}^-3$

$x \geq y$ and $x + y \leq 2$

$x + y \leq 6$, $x \geq 2$ and $y \geq 2$

$x + y \geq 4$, $x > 2$ and $y > x$

The language of sets can be conveniently applied to graphical relationships. For example, $x + y = 10$ is a straight line containing the set of ordered pairs (x, y) such that $y = 10 - x$. $x + y < 10$ is shown in the shaded area of the graph. $x + y < 10$ is the set of ordered pairs (x, y) for which $y < 10 - x$.

The solutions of equality-inequality problems are useful in advising industrial firms. These problems usually involve a large number of very simple conditions (equalities or inequalities). The method of solution involves making one of the quantities as large as possible (e.g. profit). Industrial problems are sometimes very complex, and once the conditions have been expressed algebraically, the

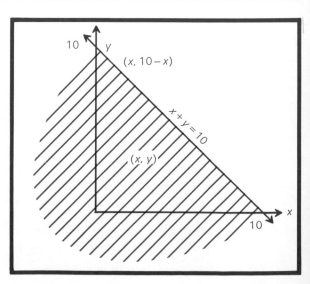

problem is solved by computer. In order to show you a simple example of these problems we have made up the following problem.

A firm manufactures two products marketed as:

Baby Powder (P) and Blackboard Chalk (C)

(1) The total production capacity is 10 tons a day of both products together. The firm is under contract to make (2) at least 3 tons of Baby Powder every day and (3) at least 4 tons of Blackboard Chalk every day. (4) Each ton of Baby Powder required 20 machine hours in production (for example 20 machines for one hour or 10 machines for two hours and so on). Each ton of Blackboard Chalk requires 80 machine hours in production. The number of men and machines available is such that not more than 560 machine hours can be worked each day. (5) The whole of the firm's output can be sold. The profit on each ton of Baby Powder sold is £5 ($12.00) and the profit on each ton of Blackboard Chalk sold is £10 ($24.00).

Find how many tons of Baby Powder and how many tons of Blackboard Chalk the firm should make every day to obtain the greatest profit. Express each condition in algebraic terms. Let x be the number of tons of P and y the number of tons of C made each day. The conditions (1) to (5) expressed algebraically are:

(1) $0 \leq x + y \leq 10$ *(2) $x \geq 3$*

(3) $y \geq 4$ *(4) $20x + 80y \leq 560$*

(5) Profit = $5x + 10y$

Entering each of these on graph paper (x axis: 0 to 12, y axis: 0 to 12) we obtain the following graph.

The common solution to conditions (1), (2), (3) and (4) is shown as the shaded area on the graph, a quadrilateral. Since Profit (5) is linear, its graph will be a plane. This plane intersects the right prism whose base is ABCD. To maximize profit we need to determine which co-ordinates of the vertices of the quadrilateral ABCD give the largest value for (5).

A = (3, 4)   *5 (3) + 10 (4) = 55*

B = (6, 4)   *5 (6) + 10 (4) = 70*

C = (4, 6)   *5 (4) + 10 (6) = 80*

D = (3, 6¼)   *5 (3) + 10 (6.25) = 77.5*

The highest profit (£80 or $192) per day results when x = 4 and y = 6. In other words, for maximum profit this company should produce each day

4 tons of Baby Powder and

6 tons of Blackboard Chalk.

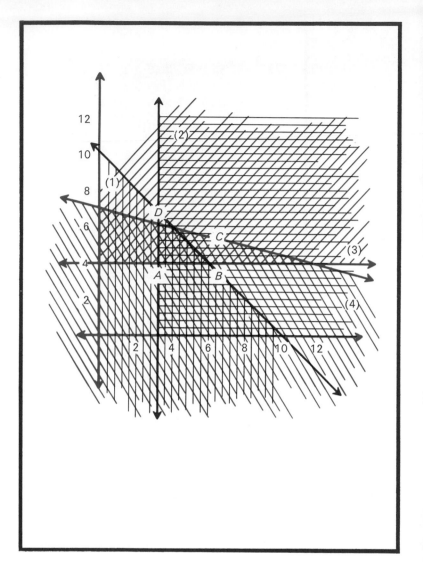

9-9. Statistics

This is a subject which will also require further reading for those who teach it. Here is a summary of important points which arise from the brief background experience we have supplied in "Patterns in Statistics."

Normal patterns of distribution are not obtained from small (rather select) samples, like those obtained at a teachers' workshop. Block or column graphs are more appropriate for these smaller samples – only in special conditions would one use a continuous line graph. A continuous line graph would not be used for a frequency distribution unless the sample was 500 or more.

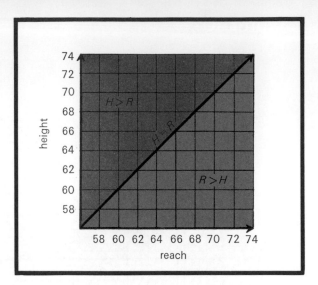

Central Tendencies

It is important to decide which of the central tendencies is appropriate for a given experiment. The *median* is the middle data when the information is ordered, or the point midway between the two middle data if there is an even number.

The *mode* – most popular data, is of vital importance to manufacturers. So also is the distribution as a whole including the range and extreme values.

The *arithmetic mean* is commonly known as the arithmetic average. Calculation of the arithmetic mean can either be done directly from information collected or from a convenient guessed mean – with appropriate correction. Eleven-year-old students suggested this method for themselves to avoid heavy calculation. Deviations ($\pm$) from the *guessed mean* (usually a convenient whole number of units) are summed and the total deviation is divided by the number of observations and added or subtracted from the guessed mean. For information other than central tendencies, such as standard deviation, we recommend you read a basic textbook.

Ordering a mass of statistical information is important. Students should begin with a little data first. Sometimes information needs to be grouped. In recording the weights of a set of 50 men ranging from 140 lbs. to 240 lbs. the weights might be grouped in intervals of 5 lbs. (140-144, 145-149, 150-154, etc.).

The effects of this grouping of data can be seen by comparing histograms for grouping in 2 lbs., 10 lbs. and 50 lbs. (see p. 90) intervals. It is possible to mask individual differences too much by grouping in large intervals. Histogram is the correct term for a frequency block graph. It should not be used for other types of block graphs.

Correlation Graphs or Scattergrams

Comparing two sets of information on a graph often leads to interesting discussion. We have chosen a representation of height-reach in *Patterns in Statistics.* In a representation of this type it is important to label *spaces* (1″ unit if possible) and not lines, to allow room to show the frequency in each square. In this particular investigation it is advisable to use the same range on each axis. Some data, Reach 67, Height 70 occur several times. These can be marked by crosses using different colours for men and women. You will see that the *squares*, points where the height and reach are equal, lie along the diagonal. The *tall rectangles* (those with height greater than reach) lie above the diagonal, and the *wide rectangles* lie below the diagonal. There is a clustering of results about the diagonal because few people show a very great variation in height and reach. Students and teachers sometimes represent these results very effectively by means of a 3-dimensional graph using a geo-board and stacking washers on the pegs. The frequency (number of people in each square) can be shown by vertical columns. To make a 3-dimensional graph you could use structural material such as Unifix. A correlation graph for skin area and volume would show far less clustering since this information was *estimated* and not measured.

Chapter 10

Keeping Track: Planning, Assessing, Reporting

10-1   Planning Students' Progress   188

10-2   Assessing Students' Progress   189

10-3   Reporting Students' Progress   191

Keeping Track: Planning, Assessing, Reporting

"Man is the measure of all things." Protagoras

Traditionally, the measurement of students' progress has been determined by the use of formal examinations at intervals to establish levels of achievement based on a 100-point scale. If a pupil scored a predetermined score or better, it was assumed that he was sufficiently well prepared to begin a new section. Professor W. W. Sawyer comments that knowing about half of the work from the previous year does not provide a firm enough foundation for anything, let alone advanced study. Then there is the problem of deciding whether a *fifty-percenter* should be promoted and a *forty-niner* should fail and be required to repeat the work. Gradually, teachers have become convinced that the percentage system of marking is utterly unrealistic and too arbitrary. At the same time teachers lost confidence in their own ability to make value judgments. Following the lead of Dr. E. L. Thorndike, measurement experts advertised the fact that teachers' marks were thoroughly unreliable and that objective tests were the only means to sensible evaluation.

Standardized tests became one of the chief instruments of measurement, particularly in the United States and Canada. Because these were considered objective and thus free of the judgment factor, they were used to measure intelligence, reading ability, spelling skills, computation, comprehension — in fact, almost every aspect of the child's intellectual development. Teachers and parents attached a great deal of importance to the results obtained; an importance that was in no way justified by the attempts of the test makers to be objective or by the methods they used to standardize these tests. One of the main techniques used to validate the intelligence test was to correlate the test scores against teachers' marks, even after it had been stated that teachers' marks were unreliable. It seemed as if the measurement experts were more interested in the new plaything of statistics than they were in the children.

One of the major consequences of the dominance of standardized tests has been the allocation of particular skills and concepts to certain grade levels. This assignment of specific topics or skills to particular grade levels has been a straitjacket which has stifled thought and restricted the curriculum for many years. Mastery by pupils of skills and concepts appearing on standardized tests became the annual objective of teachers. Because of this, instruction technique has been largely that of "teach-drill-test-reteach-drill-test." It has caused teachers and others to underestimate the power and extent of students' thinking and students have indeed become in the words of Maria Montessori ". . . butterflies mounted on pins, . . . spreading the useless wings of barren and meaningless knowledge which they have acquired."

It was the apparent infallibility attached to professionally constructed standardized tests that caused teachers to lose confidence in their own judgment. When nothing was done to restore this confidence, there was a tendency on the part of teachers to stop using their personal knowledge and understanding of each child as a mediating influence on the results obtained by standardized tests. The curriculum became rigid and millions of children received their doses of instruction from the same spoon. The result of such a rigid curriculum was an accumulation of facts and figures for which pupils' mastery could be easily tested.

A teaching technique was needed to transfer these facts and figures to the students. Educational theorists developed several "efficient" ways to speed up this transfer of knowledge. Thorndike and his contemporaries concluded that knowledge was made up of little pieces and that if you took each little piece, one at a time, and concentrated on it, learning would be faster and could be easily measured. This was followed by the theory of the associationists. They believed you should teach several things at the same time so that by interrelation and overlap, more information could be learned more efficiently. This theory had the value that on an examination, if one question stimulated the retrieval of one bit of information, the other ideas that were associated with it would also be available. Another theory combines some of the features of the two mentioned. Knowledge is divided into little pieces and related to all the other pieces, then presented in a sequence interspersed with reinforcement. Dr. Wilfred Wees describes this sequence of pieces as a program, and the technique is called programmed learning.

The concept of the mind as a receptacle is not consistent with recent thinking on learning. It does not reflect the demands of our society. Society requires ". . . minds that are not walled-in reservoirs of a knowledge . . . but minds that are organized forces of effective energy . . ."† Today we think of the mind as the source of thought and to educate is to nurture the power of thought. Therefore we should not place our test's emphasis on facts but on the child's ability to organize his thoughts toward a solution of a given situation.

†*Children, Classrooms, Curriculum, and Change,* Committee on the Scope and Organization of the Curriculum (Toronto, Ontario Curriculum Institute, 1966), p. 23.

Students should no longer be placed into grades based on preconceived adult notions of what they should learn. Neither should the omnipresent examination serve as the main prod or motivator to a more intense effort. Fear of failure is neither desirable nor effective as a motivational force for children. As a matter of fact, it may not be the child who fails. It might be the teacher who fails when the child does not achieve according to his capabilities.

Evaluation must change both in function and form if it is to guarantee the flexibility that is essential to a program that provides for the continuous progress of all children. Its function is to determine the effectiveness of the program in the development of each individual; its form is the daily observation of each pupil's interests and activities, problems and successes. Specific techniques for this kind of evaluation are now being developed. The suggestions offered in this chapter have worked for some teachers. They are intended only as starting points for experiment or discussion.

10-1. Planning Students' Progress

When a school is changing from a traditional to a child-centered program, each teacher should be given every encouragement to experiment in any field of mathematics which appeals to him or in which he feels reasonably secure. Frequently, as this approach spreads throughout the school, children's work will be examined and discussed by other members of the staff who will attempt to use the good ideas. This is an inevitable interim stage. Students, conditioned by several years of being told precisely what to do and then given the answers, will take longer to adjust to the opportunity of doing some thinking for themselves. Almost any new experience will prove of value to them. A visitor to the school may think that the mathematics program is chaotic and lacks progression. This condition may last a year or even longer until teachers and children have sufficient experience to be confident and reasonably objective about achievement. Then the principal and teachers will be ready to come together to plan a basic curriculum. They may choose to do this under headings such as concepts, experiences, materials required, and vocabulary. After an interval for classroom experiment, comparison of children's work will reveal stages of development in their learning, as well as difficulties and successes. Such a procedure helps teachers to sort out, in broad terms, the order in which children form concepts. But it must be emphasized once more that the mathematics program should be flexible. Ideally, teachers from neighbouring elementary and secondary schools should be involved in the development of major mathematical topics.

10-2. Assessing Students' Progress

"What appears certain is that our traditional educational measuring instruments fail to function adequately in the new situation, and we are far from devising new instruments of assessment to serve the new situation."[†] While this quotation is taken from Britain's latest secondary school project for less able students *(Mathematics for the Majority)* it is equally true for all schools including the brightest students. As mentioned earlier, teachers feel insecure about subjective assessment — yet ask any teacher who has taught a child for one month or more about the child's capabilities and he will give a discerning reply. If he has been using activity learning he will probably also be able to provide many details about the child's previous experiences. With practice, teachers can become more confident and skilled in this kind of assessment. At this time, we will isolate some of those factors that we wish to evaluate.

Computational Skill

Consider the most familiar — the ability to compute efficiently. This requires knowledge of basic number facts. By far the most important of these are the addition and subtraction trios extended to 100 (and subsequently beyond). Before they are memorized these will first be recognized as patterns. To find out whether a child knows the basic addition or subtraction trios, ask him orally. Application of the commutative law of addition is essential since it reduces the number of facts to be memorized.

A knowledge of multiplication and division facts is also essential, but response should not be expected until addition and subtraction facts are known. Knowledge of these facts is not measured

by the speed with which a student can repeat the facts in order. It is more important that he should respond accurately. He should also be able to apply the commutative law of multiplication.

Tests in computational skill can be of the traditional type provided the children understand and appreciate the need for them. These tests can also measure children's understanding of the varied situations in which different computational methods should be applied. This kind of evaluation should be part of the learning program and be jointly planned by the students and the teacher. It should provide for self-evaluation as well as for diagnosis of individual difficulties.

Understanding of Concepts

Concepts such as conservation of number and so on are only acquired after considerable and varied experience. Checks[†] to see whether a child has acquired a concept; for example, conservation of length, should be made by employing careful questioning and using real materials. The acquisition of some concepts by students may be examined by questioning alone. Frequently, it is possible to judge whether a concept has been acquired by more informal methods — while a student is experimenting with materials or when he is recording results in his own words.

A headmaster of a large junior school in Britain discussed the simplest method of keeping records of each child's progress with the teachers in his school. For each class they drew up a list of concepts on a large sheet of paper and listed each child's name. This check list worked well for this school.

Process or Solution

Most instruments of evaluation are concerned solely with the end product or answer. Rarely do such tests attempt any measure of the process used to arrive at an answer. Students should be encouraged to do their computations in a variety of ways

[†]The Nuffield Mathematics Teaching Project in Britain has collaborated with Professor Piaget's School in Geneva to produce a series of check-ups for teachers to give children when teachers are in doubt as to whether children have acquired a certain concept or not. Many of the first check-ups concern conservation and an understanding of vocabulary such as thick, thin, etc.

[†]*Monograph,* Schools' Council Secondary School Mathematics Project (London, The Schools' Council Publications Company, 1968).

189

and to evaluate their own methods. This activity often provides teachers with another check for assessing the degree of understanding a student has of the operation being considered. Posing a problem relevant to a pupil's experience is often a better method of assessing the process.

Most teachers know the difficulty students have in attempting to apply a set pattern of steps to the solution of a problem. Comments such as "I did well in computation but I just couldn't do the problems" emphasizes the fallacy of attempting to channel children's thinking into rigid patterns predetermined by adults. Attempts to remedy the situation by increasing the number of problems in order to implant the steps to the solution very nearly created "innumeracy" to accompany illiteracy in schools.

Fear of mathematics was generated by the *one-way-to-do-it* approach to the solution of problems. So much energy was wasted attempting to remember the pattern of solution, that students failed to apply the *common sense* that would have eliminated the difficulty in many cases. Consider this problem: If a telephone pole 57 feet in length falls across a highway so that $17^3/_6$ feet extend from one side and $14^9/_{17}$ feet from the other, how wide is the highway? The answer supplied by a less able student reveals more thought than the *right* answer sought by the examiner. *"It seems like an awfully silly way to measure the width of the highway. I didn't even try to answer it because it didn't say whether the pole had fallen straight across or not."*

Checking concepts by careful questioning and using real materials

It is difficult to measure creativity

Creativity and Originality

This is perhaps the hardest attribute to assess and yet it is one of the most important factors in estimating mathematical potential. Creativity involves process as well as product and it is the process that is most difficult to measure. It is the student's perception of the problem and his behaviour in seeking the solution that reveals his facility with the creative process. Teachers have experimented with various forms of assessment of mathematical creativity. None has been entirely satisfactory, but here are two different ideas which have been tried.

Some teachers keep a diary or notebook of significant conversation and remarks made by children while they are experimenting with materials. Others make use of tape recorders to gather the same sort of evidence. Other teachers make a folder for each child at the beginning of his school career. Into this the teachers file any piece of work which they regard as significant in revealing a child's development, particularly concerning creativity and originality.

The first method is particularly valuable for young children and many teachers keep records of this kind. The second method has the disadvantage that children's files tend to become bulky. They need to be sorted at least once a year to ensure that only the work that is most significant in showing children's progress is retained. This type of record is invaluable for informing a new teacher of the kind of work that has been done when a student transfers from one school to another. It is also extremely useful for parent-teacher interviews when the progress of a son or daughter is being discussed.

Self Assessment

Evaluation, as part of the learning program, is often planned jointly by the teacher and the students and provides for self-evaluation as well as for diagnosis. Many teachers have found that children, when they become stimulated and involved in the work they are doing, also show interest in their own progress. Personal records of the work they have done challenge them to make greater efforts as the following example shows.

A teacher of ten-year-olds asked the class to help plan the following six weeks' work. The children were accustomed to working informally in small friendship groups and they planned the work to suit each group's needs. Each child kept a record of his progress. Later, the teacher and the children were surprised to find that the class worked so strenuously at the mathematics they had planned that they finished in half the allotted time. The teacher attributed this to the fact that every child knew what was expected of him and where he was going. Many interesting problems arose during this period which different groups were able to pursue much beyond the scope of the original plan.

We can not do better than to conclude this section on evaluation by again stating one of Professor Piaget's contentions concerning concept formation. Children are not wrong; they merely respond to the stimulus according to their knowledge and development at the particular time when we are checking their progress. If teachers keep this in mind they will give every child the encouragement he requires to gain confidence in his own abilities and to realize his maximum potential.

10-3. Reporting Students' Progress

Parents are the most valuable resource that teachers have in developing a program that meets the complex needs of each individual student. The more teachers and parents understand each other, the less a child is pulled between the two lives he is asked to live; one at home, the other at school. The key to success is communication.

Unfortunately, parent-teacher communication has frequently been limited to formal report cards, telephone calls or short notes about behaviour or subject matter difficulties. Teachers should welcome the parents' natural interest in the progress and achievements of their children and must provide parents with a meaningful assessment or report of their child's progress. More and more teachers are reporting achievement in descriptive rather than numerical terms and are including comments on adjustment to school as well. In some schools reports are being made to both students and parents. This procedure has had the happy effect of developing a much deeper sense of responsibility on the part of the students for their own progress. The suggestions for communication between the home and the school which follow may serve to strengthen this parent-teacher partnership.

Report Forms

In choosing the form that a report should take, consideration must be given to what it is intended to do. Is it for parents or for the child? If it is for parents, does it really communicate a measure of the growth of the child over a specific period? If it is for the child, is it really the most effective *pat-on-the-back* or *prod* that you can devise? If a report card is necessary, consider an anecdotal or achievement profile such as this:

Name_____ Date_____

| Work Completed | Strong Points | Particular Difficulties |

Comments:_____

_____

Teacher_____

These could be completed in duplicate, with the original mailed to the parents and a copy retained by the teacher.

Another reporting form is one that is more detailed. The advantage of this type of form is that its check list characteristic enables teachers to send home a great amount of information while not requiring an unreasonable amount of time to write up the report. (See figure p. 193.)

Teachers should not confine their ideas of reporting to report cards. Perhaps the most reliable indicator of progress is the student's own work. A file of significant samples used to guide the teacher in his own assessment of a student often provides the best evidence of progress for the parents. Completed projects or assignments, models and reports on research undertaken should be taken home and shared with parents. Some measure of the depth of understanding that a student achieves is revealed when he explains a piece of work to his parents.

Short notes commending honest effort on the part of the student should be even more common than those identifying weakness or difficulty. Even though teachers must be honest with parents, it is important that parents should not become conditioned to expect that every communication from the school means that something is wrong. They appreciate knowing when things are going well, too.

Teacher-Parent Interviews

When formal report cards are being altered to reflect more closely the staff's philosophy of education, it is necessary to discuss the changes with the parents. If, in fact, the report is intended for parents, there is no good reason why it should not be handed directly to them. This sets the stage for establishing even better communication through parent-teacher interviews.

Interviewing should be for the parents of all students, not merely for those whose children are having difficulty. Every pupil is entitled to the benefits that come to him when his teachers and parents work together. Many purposes can be served by the meeting of teacher and parents. The great advantage to the school program of interviewing is that every teacher can be involved. The value of these interviews is largely dependent on the attitudes each teacher brings. While it is impossible to set a common standard, there are some basic tenets that should be considered when preparing for an interview.

1/ *A deep respect for parents. Any teacher who honestly feels that the great majority of parents have the best interests of their children at heart is off to a good start in building friendly and useful relationships with them.*

2/ *Teachers must convince parents of their sincere desire to do the best they can for their boys and girls. What is best can only be achieved when teacher and parents talk together about the things that occur in the home and school life of the child.*

3/ *The school exists for children. Teachers must begin by understanding each pupil as an individual. This is the fundamental reason for teacher and parents to get together.*

4/ *Parents must be accepted as they are. This acceptance is based upon a genuine willingness to let people be themselves.*

Classroom Visitation

One of the most effective, yet seldom used ways of interpreting the school program to parents is to invite them to school to observe their children in action. Usually this approach is reserved for special occasions such as Education Week, Parents' Day, a concert or play. It should happen much more

STUDENT DEVELOPMENT APPRAISAL

Columns: Lang. Arts | Social Science | Math | Science | French | Cons. Ed. | Art | Music | Ind. Arts Home Ec. | Typing | Phys. & Health Ed.

I INDEPENDENT STUDY AND INQUIRY

INITIATIVE
- is a self-starter
- needs some direction
- needs prodding

- shows curiosity
- is inventive
- shows some originality

PERSEVERANCE
- finishes the task
- discourages easily
- projects often are not completed

ORGANIZATIONAL ABILITY
- uses time efficiently
- plans well with help
- wastes time

AWARENESS
- shows concern for others
- is safety conscious
- uses equipment properly
- is careless

II SMALL GROUP ACTIVITY

ORAL COMMUNICATION
- is articulate
- understands and is understood
- is often misunderstood

WRITTEN COMMUNICATION
- is a clear concise, imaginative writer
- writes well
- has difficulty in self expression
- is often incoherent

CO-OPERATION
- tends to be overbearing
- shares leadership
- accepts the rule of the majority
- has difficulty working with others

PARTICIPATION
- takes part eagerly
- contributes to the group
- is rather quiet but alert
- is a passive spectator

RESPONSIBILITY
- is well prepared
- is usually dependable
- is unreliable

III MASTERY OF CONCEPTS

Here the student is evaluated with respect to the fulfilment of his individual potential.

- Exceptional
- Very Good
- Acceptable
- Less Than Acceptable

IV DEVELOPMENT OF SKILLS

- Exceptional
- Very Good
- Acceptable
- Less Than Acceptable

V PHYSICAL FITNESS

This is evaluated by a series of standardized tests established by the Canadian Association for Physical and Health Education. Generally the results indicate that this student's level of fitness is:

Excellent ☐   Very Good ☐   Good ☐   Fair ☐   Below Standard ☐

Detailed results are available from the student.

frequently and for no special reason. Parents gain valuable insight and are more inclined to support the school program when they observe their child in his *other life.* Initially, it helps the parent if the teacher explains what is happening and the purpose behind the activity. This is a matter of courtesy but it is more than that. It suggests the teacher's willingness to have parents comment about what is being done and demonstrates respect for their opinions.

Many parents with special skills and abilities should be invited to become actively involved in the school program. This is a community resource that is commonly ignored and yet often has tremendous potential. It is good both for the program and public relations. Here again, the initiative must be taken by the teacher since many parents would equate volunteering with interference. Find out what resources are available; decide how they can be used to advantage in the school program; then approach the parent with a request for assistance. The response may surprise you.

Comparisons

While we may have been overly critical of the traditional devices for measuring progress in this chapter, it was done deliberately and for a specific purpose. When comparisons are being made between pupils in an active learning program and those in a traditional one, nearly always the pupils of both programs will be tested with a traditional test. Since the objectives of the two types of programs differ so widely, it makes little sense to apply a technique that was designed to measure the degree of success in only one program. What is needed is some serious research on the problem of devising appropriate methods for evaluating the growth of students using the active learning approach. There are encouraging signs that research institutions are directing some of their energies toward research concerned with the problems in education. Dr. T. C. O'Brien of Boston University has begun to investigate divergent productive thinking in children. No doubt there are many others who are concerned with the problems that face educators who are attempting to use the active learning approach. During the period of transition, teachers need the reassurance that suitable tests and other devices for evaluation are being prepared.

Chapter 11

A Look at the Future

11-1   Integration   197

11-2   Secondary Schools   198

11-3   Teacher Training   199

11-4   In-Service Training and Professional   201
       Associations

Chapter 11   A Look at the Future

"We could wish no child a happier fate than to encounter, as many do, a good teacher."
Children and their Primary Schools

This book has been written for teachers. Using mathematics as the vehicle, we have tried to present a variety of ideas and techniques that will enable educators to bridge the gap between the traditional, teacher-dominated, rigidly organized classroom and the more modern, child-centered, flexible program that provides for the active involvement of every child. We have emphasized that there is no one way to begin or to continue the development of such a program. Good teachers will revise and adapt suggestions to suit themselves and the children they teach. As they gain experience and their faith in this approach to learning is confirmed, they will move far beyond the resources of this book. Perhaps one day they will write a book themselves, sharing their experiences with others, and thus help their fellow teachers to move a step closer to providing education of high quality for everyone.

11-1. Integration

At the beginning we suggested that one of the aims of learning mathematics in this active, creative way was to provide opportunities for children to discover the order and pattern which is the very essence of mathematics, not only in the man-made world, but in the natural world as well. One of the most important responsibilities of teachers is to help children see order and pattern in experience. Rigid division of the curriculum into subjects tends to interrupt the thought patterns of children, causes them to lose interest, and prevents them from identifying the common elements in problem solving. These are among the many reasons why most learning experiences should cut across the traditional subject disciplines.

While we have concerned ourselves principally with mathematics and with other aspects of the curriculum which readily give rise to mathematics, especially science, this is an artificial distinction which boys and girls do not make. Children's learning does not fit into subject categories. For them, learning is an undivided whole. As students advance in school, the different disciplines become more relevant, but even at this later stage, subjects merge and overlap.

Those teachers who began working in a more creative way with mathematics and science found that this approach soon spread to other areas in the curriculum. Subject barriers as well as lesson barriers became blurred. The next step was to experiment with an *integrated* day. Children were encouraged to follow their own interests until they were ready to put the work aside. One of the most effective ways of integrating the curriculum is to relate it through the use of the environment (natural, man-made, or structured by the teacher) to the boundless curiosity which children have about the world around them. This method of planning the day, with several different activities, is exciting for the children, but it requires the teacher to keep careful records to ensure that over a week or a longer period, a balance is maintained for every child. This task is easier if the children themselves take some part in this record keeping. The approach utilizing the experience and interests of children also requires thoughtful planning in the selection of materials and of questions to act as productive starting points.

Mathematical units or topics contribute to many other aspects of the curriculum, especially science (from which they are often inseparable), geography, history and creative writing. Conversely, units in other subjects make contributions to the teaching of mathematics. These include physical education, art and craft (particularly work in three dimensions), and music. Active and creative learning, in which opportunities are provided by teachers for students to think for themselves, is applicable to every aspect of the curriculum. This has been ably demonstrated by hundreds of teachers in Great Britain. This does not mean that there is no place for learning and sharpening skills, but that practice follows, and does not precede, concept formation and understanding.

Learning through individual and small-group investigations is applicable for all ages from kindergarten to postgraduate, and for all levels of ability from the slowest to the most able. This does not imply that all students must follow the same path. Some will require extensive experience with real materials whenever a new idea or concept is introduced; others need little. But at all stages, even when the learning aids are only paper and pencil, the form of the question should challenge the students to think and to explore for themselves. For the majority of students, as they progress through the secondary and tertiary levels, emphasis will shift from work with real materials to problems which, while challenging in themselves, can be solved in a variety of practical ways or by a combination of practical and abstract methods.

11-2. Secondary Schools

Reference was made in Chapter 2 to the special problems faced by teachers in secondary schools, particularly during the transitional period of change from teaching by lecture methods (however good) to more active learning by individual students. With the changes in mathematical content brought about by new demands of industry and the business community, and with the increasing availability of the computer or computer time, mathematics promises to be an exciting subject with a wide appeal to many students.

In Great Britain a working party of members of the Mathematical Association and business leaders has facilitated working visits of mathematics teachers to industrial firms for periods ranging from a few weeks to a year. This has made it possible for teachers to see mathematics in action and to gain some insight into the requirements of industry. Without exception, industrial firms desire applicants who have not only specific knowledge of mathematics but the ability to think and to create mathematical problems as well as to solve them. Fortunately, this demand is in complete agreement with the educational aims of the in-service program we have already described.

We have tried to introduce teachers of children of different ages to some of the new topics in mathematics by guided discovery techniques. If we had had access to a computer we should have provided opportunities for designing a simple flow chart and trying this out on a computer. It is our belief that most students and teachers would enjoy the experience and that it would give them some insight into modern practices in industry.

Our introduction to these topics: sets, vectors, groups, graphs, and linear programming, has been brief, and some important concepts (rings, fields and matrices) have not been included either because of time or because of other requests made by teachers. Many of these topics already form part of the secondary school program in addition to the differential and integral calculus and properties of conic sections. All these afford scope for exploration and discovery in the initial stages. We hope that these methods will be applied

later as the subject becomes more axiomatic. Many books are available to provide assistance with content, but few give help on classroom presentation. Perhaps those secondary school teachers who have been planning and experimenting with a flexible, discovery-oriented program for older students are ready to share their experience with other teachers. One thing is certain. The pattern of instruction in secondary schools must change if it is to meet the needs of pupils coming from elementary schools. Boys and girls who have been given the opportunity to think for themselves and who have responded to the challenge will not conform to the traditional lecture method, nor will the present curriculum provide for their interests and needs.

A Look
at the
Future

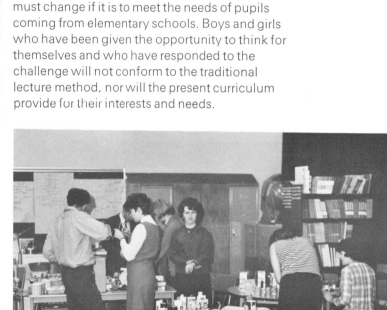

Older student helping younger children in an ungraded program

Student teachers participating in discovery learning

11-3. Teacher Training

If fully qualified, experienced teachers find it necessary to participate in discovery learning of mathematics to convince themselves that the method is feasible and right for the children they teach, then teachers-in-training will require similar and more prolonged experience. In addition, many student teachers lack confidence in their own background knowledge of mathematics when they enter college and some time must be allocated for extending this knowledge.

In the classroom, learning through individual or small-group investigation makes heavy demands on experienced teachers. Classroom practice for student teachers requires very careful planning

199

if they are not to be overwhelmed. It is important to keep in mind that most of these young adults have never experienced the freedom that this kind of learning demands. A gradual beginning is essential. In the first instance, if the student teacher prepares a topic for two or, at most, four children, he can observe them working, listen to their comments, and ask questions which will help them discover the answer for themselves. Inexperienced as well as experienced teachers have to convince themselves through their own work with children that there is no need to tell the answer provided children are given appropriate experience and asked the right questions. Later, the student teacher needs to work with groups of gradually increasing sizes—perhaps 8, then 16 children—before he takes over a whole class and plans group work for them.

Some new school buildings have sensibly made provision for learning bases or areas of various kinds and sizes. These include classrooms, small study centres and large open areas. Resource centres contain a vast array of teaching aids that are readily accessible to students and teachers. These aids, besides books and pictures, include radios, films, filmstrips, 2″ × 2″ slides, sound recordings on tape and records, programmed materials, television, microscopes, and apparatus of all kinds. Wise teachers regard these teaching aids as tools for learning and not as crutches to compensate for weak or ineffective instruction. The exciting new designs in school construction are important in that they allow much more scope for co-operative teaching. No longer do a teacher and his class exist in isolation. Student teachers need to have experience as members of a team. Whether it is composed of two beginners and an experienced teacher or any other combination of talents makes little difference. The co-operative planning of learning experiences necessitates greater attention to objectives and leads teachers to adapt classroom procedures to meet these objectives. While relatively few newly trained teachers can expect to enjoy these ideal physical surroundings, they should develop confidence in their own ability to participate as a member of a team whatever the limitations imposed by concrete and brick.

At all levels of education we must *practice what we preach.* Children learn more about co-operation

and democratic living by what a person does than what he says. So it is with student teachers. Lectures about co-operative planning, flexible child-centered programs and freedom to learn will achieve little unless the prospective teachers have the opportunity to live and learn in the kind of atmosphere they are expected to recreate. In spite of the all-too-frequent limitations of old and over-crowded buildings, the lack of time, and external controls, the colleges should provide an environment which will be a model for teachers to imitate. The classroom should be a place in which there is an atmosphere of mutual trust and respect, where children are encouraged to question and discuss, to read and observe, to plan and experiment.

An area for the individual showing of 16 mm. films

A learning area of a new school

11-4. In-service Training and Professional Associations

The approach to the teaching of mathematics and other disciplines has undergone far-reaching changes. Content, especially in the secondary schools, has also changed and may continue to do so. This means that regular retraining of teachers is essential. It is important that opportunities for further education be made available to all teachers, and that some effort be made to co-ordinate and integrate the various courses and conferences that originate from universities, faculties of education, professional associations, local school boards and others. There is a need too, for professional counselling services to assist young teachers in choosing the most appropriate program. While professional organizations, both general and specific, have always played a part in encouraging their members to improve their qualifications, the present situation of rapid and accelerating change provides a wonderful opportunity for strong and sensitive leadership that will lead to greater influence and eventual autonomy in the certification of teachers.

The acceptance, by teachers, of the responsibility for a truly professional approach to teaching has led them to seek new knowledge and new techniques that will improve their competence in the classroom. Perhaps the greatest improvement results from discussion, demonstrations and consultation with colleagues, principals and others. This is particularly effective when it is related to the problems identified by the teacher concerned. Other informal ways that teachers use to keep up-to-date include private reading, travel, service on curriculum committees, intervisitation, attendance at conferences, and participation in curriculum research.

With growing professionalism on the part of teachers comes a willingness on the part of school authorities to recognize in-service activities as a necessary part of a teacher's work. They are more inclined to make time available during the school day and to share expenses for attendance at seminars, conferences and special courses when there is evidence that such a practice does improve the quality of education in their schools.

Freedom
to
Learn

There are many opportunities for joint action on the part of teachers and trustees that will nourish the *partnership* relationship in the field of educational progress. There is a great need for teacher centres and experimental schools which will be accessible to all teachers in an area. Teacher centres are places where teachers can come together for discussion, working sessions, preparation of topics for the classroom, display of pupils' work, and in-service activities of all kinds. Experimental or model schools are necessary because we lack convincing models of the kind of classroom environment we want to create. Parents everywhere need to be shown how things could be different, because they are rightly suspicious of theories and experiments. What is needed are functioning schools that would demonstrate to the public and to educators the kind of learning that we have attempted to describe in this book. They should be schools that can develop and grow over a period of time, not just demonstration classes. They should be schools that people could go and see, that visiting teachers could work in; schools that demonstrate convincing alternatives to the traditional model that is a part of the experience of most people. The planning and implementation of such a project requires a degree of co-operation and understanding that has been all too rare in educational practice. The fact that it is and will be occurring in many jurisdictions augurs well for the future.

We mentioned earlier that the teacher is no longer isolated in his classroom. We could go further and claim that co-operative effort should extend across a school system. With recent technological advances, it is possible for groups of teachers to communicate across counties and countries. International co-operation through teacher exchange programs and the sharing of experiences through publications, radio and television brings the diversified resources of many nations within reach of those who wish to use them. The professional teacher should be regarded as a vital component of a team that has tremendous potential as an educative force, whether it be focussed locally, nationally or internationally. If today's school is to be not a relic of the past but a beacon for the future, it is the classroom teacher who will make it so.

Happiness is learning

Index

a

accuracy, 92, 121, 125
active learning, definition, 16
addition, 102, 118
additive identity, 167
angles, exterior, 98, 100
    interior, 98, 100
    of regular polygons, 152
Archimedes' Principle, 146
area, 9, 15, 81, 84, 99, 121
    of surface, 50, 84, 91
arithmetic mean, 148, 184
assessment, 189
    creativity and originality, 191
    of self, 189
assignment cards, 14, 15, 20, 94
associationists, 188
associative laws, 167
    of addition, 167
    of multiplication, 167
averages, 148

b

basic laws for the set of rational numbers, 167
basic number facts, 113
battleship, 51
biased sampling, 148
Blackie, John, 7

c

capacity, 13, 29, 77, 81, 82
cardinal number, 166
central tendency, 91, 92, 148, 184
circles, 97, 156, 173
    growth of, 129
circumference, 15, 122
classroom visitation, 192
Clegg, Alec, 8
closed question, 15
coin-tossing cumulative graph, 148
common base line, 140
commutative laws, 167
    of addition, 167
    of multiplication, 167
comparison, 121, 131
computation, 117
    skill in, 189
cones, 97, 98, 173
congruence, 153, 173, 176
conservation, 9, 121, 123, 127, 147
    of number, 112
    of volume, 131
cubes, 20, 50, 97, 100, 123, 124, 156, 173
    growth of, 155
cuboids, 50, 97, 123
    growth of, 155
cylinders, 50, 97, 173

d

decimals, 167
density, 91, 145, 146, 147
developmental questions for limits, 97
   for similarity, 97
   for symmetry, 94
Dewey, John, 44
diameter, 15, 122
diamonds, 173
Dienes, Zoltan P., 3, 116
disjoint set, 168
distance, 122
distribution of data, 148
distributive law, 167
division, 119, 170
Dr. Nim, 52

e

enlargement, 173
equal units, 124, 140
equations, 170, 172
equilateral triangle, 97, 157
equipment, 19, 23, 24, 31, 32, 44, 49, 77
   lists of, 32-34
equivalence of fractions, 166
expected frequency, coin, 148
   dice, 149
exponents, 169
extension of the number system, 166
exterior angles, 98, 100

f

face finding, 15
film slides, 47
films, 44-46
flotation, 146
fractions, 121, 166
   equivalence of, 166
frequency, 148
Froebel, 3
fulcrum, 144

g

Galileo, 26
games, 50-52
geo-board, 10, 15, 123, 184
golden mean, 177, 178
golden rectangle, 178
golden section, 177
gradual beginning, 19, 20, 21, 23, 29
graph, 154, 159, 183
   correlation, 184
   patterns, 99
great circle distances, 147
grouping, 21
   data, 91, 92
groups of order 4, 106
growth of squares, 129

h

height, 122
hexagon, regular, 97, 157
Holt, John, 13
Howard, John, 46

i

I Do and I Understand, 44
identity elements, 167
index of rotundity, 125
inequalities, 81, 101
infinity, 157
integers, 170
integrated day, 23, 197
interior angle, 98, 100
intersection of sets, 167
intervisitation, 143
Into Tomorrow, 46
invariance of number, 112
inverse elements, 167
   of addition, 167
   of multiplication, 167
isosceles triangle, 97

j

Justice, 71

k

kaleidoscope, the, 154

l

length, 15, 31, 77, 81, 83, 99, 119, 121
limits, 94, 97, 101, 157, 173
Lotto, 51

m

Mancala, 52
Montessori, Maria, 187
matching, one-to-one correspondence, counting, 111
Maths Alive, 44
Maths is a Monster, 46
Matthews, Geoffrey, 46
mean, 148
  arithmetic, 148, 184
  deviation from, 148
  guessed, 184
measurement, 22
  cylinder, 132
  instruments for, 32
  kinds of, 121
median, 148, 184
memorization, 7
metric month, 127
  system, 121, 127
  weights, 145
mode, 148, 184
motivation, 8
multiplication, 106, 118, 170
  square, 100, 119
  tables, 99, 159
multiplicative identity, 167

n

notation, 113
  directional signs, 170
  mathematical, 113
Nuffield Mathematics Teaching Project, 44, 46
number, cardinal, 166
  conservation of, 112
  natural, 166
  negative, 102, 106, 159
  ordinal, 166
  patterns, of, 81
number and measure relationships, 117
number line, 102

o

O'Brien, T. C., 194
100 square, 114
open-ended questions, 14, 15, 21, 22, 81, 87, 101
ordinal number, 166
out-of-line data, 92
overhead projectors, 47

p

paper folding, 149, 152, 153
parallelogram, 15, 97, 152, 174
parents, 58, 65, 66, 68, 70, 72, 73, 74
Parents' Day, 73
patterns in algebra, 101, 102
  in graphs, 99
  in groups, 101, 106
  in mathematics, 87
  in numbers, 101
  in sets, 101
  in shapes, 94
  in statistics, 87, 183, 184
pendulum, 15, 29, 100, 136, 137
perimeter, 81, 84, 87, 99, 122
  constant, 11, 99, 159
  of rectangles, 22
Pestalozzi, 3
Piaget, Jean, 8, 9, 46, 124, 147, 191
place value, 116
Polya, G., 165
polygons, 149, 173, 174
precision, 121, 125
probability, 93
properties of familiar shapes, 173
proportion, 81, 101, 147, 154, 157
Pythagorean theorem, 174

q

quadrilaterals, 97, 174

r

rate, 81, 146, 147
ratio, 81, 101, 146, 147, 157
rectangles, 15, 84, 97, 157, 173, 194
reflection, 96, 154
regrouping, 118
regular hexagon, 97, 157
reiteration of the unit, 121, 124, 131
relations, 160
release time, 68
report cards, 6, 192, 193
resource centres, 44
reversal, 9
rhombuses, 97, 152, 173, 174
rotation, 96
rotational symmetry, 154

s

Sawyer, W. W., 187
Schweitzer, Albert, 7
self assessment, 191
sensory-motor learning, 9
sequence, 100, 102, 157, 169
set, 160, 167
  disjoint, 168
  intersection of, 167, 168
  union of, 168
  universal, 167
shapes, properties of, 173
  three-dimensional, 84, 101, 122, 152, 173, 176
  two-dimensional, 122, 139, 150, 173, 176
similarity, 94, 101, 157
  and enlargement, 176
  in two dimensions, 155
  sequences of volume, area, perimeter, 155
skewing, 92
Snakes and Ladders, 50
specific gravity, 146, 147
speed, 26, 137
spheres, 97, 156
squares, 84, 97, 124, 152, 156, 157, 173, 174
  growth of, 129
standard deviation, 148
standard units, 121, 124, 125, 132, 145
standardized tests, 69, 187
statistics, 148
student teachers, 59, 61, 199
subsets, 160, 167
subtraction, 102, 118, 170
  aspects of, 102
  equal addition, 118
Sullivan, John W., 70
surface area, 50, 84, 91
symmetry, 94, 96, 101, 173
  and congruence, 176
  mirror image, 153
  of geometric shapes, 154
  rotational, 154

t

tangrams, 127
tape recorder, 49
task cards, 14, 15, 20, 94
teacher-parent interviews, 192
television, 47
tessellation, 95, 101, 130
Think a Dot, 52
Thorndike, E. L., 187, 188
tic-tac-toe, 51
tiling, 95, 101, 130
time, 26, 31, 82, 121, 177, 181
timetables, schedules, 134, 137
  school, 68, 69
total involvement, 19, 23
Tower of Hanoi, 52
training centre, 31
transformation, 180
translation, 97
triangle, 15, 173
  equilateral, 97
  isosceles, 97
  regular, 157
triangular prism, 15
Tuf, 52
200 chart, 114, 115

u

union of sets, 168
unity element, 167
universal set, 167

v

vector addition, 179
vectors, 101, 179
  displacement, 179
  force, 179
  velocity, 179
vital statistics, 80
volume, 15, 50, 84, 91, 100, 121, 146
  by displacement, 132

w

Wees, Wilfred, 188
weight, 31, 77, 81, 84, 92, 100, 146
Whittaker, Dora, 46
whole-class involvement, 21, 22
width, 15, 99, 122
workshop schedule, 62

z

zero element, 167